PRACTICAL
PHOTO-LITHOGRAPHY

PRACTICAL
PHOTO-LITHOGRAPHY

BY

C. MASON WILLY

FOURTH EDITION

EDITED AND REVISED BY G. E. MESSENGER
Member of the Technical Staff of Hunter-Penrose Ltd.

LONDON
SIR ISAAC PITMAN & SONS, LTD.

First published 1936
Second edition 1938
Third edition 1940
Fourth edition 1952
Reprinted 1954
Reprinted 1958

SIR ISAAC PITMAN & SONS, LTD.
PITMAN HOUSE, PARKER STREET, KINGSWAY, LONDON, W.C.2
THE PITMAN PRESS, BATH
PITMAN HOUSE, BOUVERIE STREE7, CARLTON, MELBOURNE
27 BECKETTS BUILDINGS, PRESIDENT STREET, JOHANNESBURG

ASSOCIATED COMPANIES
PITMAN MEDICAL PUBLISHING COMPANY, LTD.
45 NEW OXFORD STREET, LONDON, W.C.I

PITMAN PUBLISHING CORPORATION
2 WEST 45TH STREET, NEW YORK

SIR ISAAC PITMAN & SONS (CANADA), LTD.
(INCORPORATING THE COMMERCIAL TEXT BOOK COMPANY)
PITMAN HOUSE, 381–383 CHURCH STREET, TORONTO

MADE IN GREAT BRITAIN AT THE PITMAN PRESS BATH
E8—(T.105)

PREFACE TO THE FOURTH EDITION

DURING and since the Second World War, extensive research by craftsmen, managements, suppliers and manufacturers, together with a free interchange of ideas, has resulted in great progress being made not only in the production of litho printing plates and machines, but in the types of printing that the photo-lithographic process can successfully undertake. There has been a general effort to reduce the number of printings while improving tone rendering and quality. Better means of duplication have been provided and the proofing press has been made to render results as similar as possible to those given by the cylinder machine. New types of photographic originals have to be reproduced, while reproductions generally have grown to greater linear dimensions. Appropriate reference has been made to the more important of these rather complex improvements resulting from the application of new ideas, and certain new illustrations have been introduced in place of some that were definitely obsolete. Nevertheless, the basic knowledge of the process is not less important to the student for whom this work was originally compiled, and in order that it should not be denied to him it was decided, in the preparation of this new edition, to leave the general treatment practically intact and to make only the most essential amendments to the text to keep it reasonably up-to-date.

PREFACE TO THE FIRST EDITION

PHOTO-LITHOGRAPHY has made such immense progress both in its extent and usefulness during the last few years that such a book as this has been called for to give the trade the practical details of the processes now employed, which are now so far in advance of the methods described in previously published handbooks. Hitherto the information has only been obtainable in a very incomplete form in books treating of lithography in general and in articles published in the trade press. Lectures and technical instruction in the trade schools and by demonstrators of supply houses have certainly amplified this information, but have only conveyed it in an oral way, so that the dissemination of the knowledge was necessarily limited. The author of this work has sought to remedy this defect by collecting together all available information on the subject so as to provide a complete guide to the most recent developments of photo-lithography. The book will not only be of service to apprentices and workmen who have actually to carry out the processes, but will furnish the employer, director, manager and foreman with a full explanation of the processes and of the apparatus, chemicals and materials employed, so that they may understand the routine and thereby supervise the work in all its stages.

The author has had extensive experience as a demonstrator of the processes he describes, and is therefore well able to realize the necessity of presenting the subject in a clearly understandable way, without assuming much if any previous knowledge by the reader.

It will be noted that not only black and white reproduction in half-tone and line is dealt with, but that also the latest methods of colour work are very fully treated, and the principal bypaths of the photo-lithographic process are explored. The chapters on lithographic and group printing will be found particularly useful and up-to-date. It has naturally been impossible within the compass of the work to describe the numerous forms of step and repeat apparatus now available, but the general principles of their working will be understood from the descriptions given.

Photo-lithography has now so many ramifications and applications that in the limited dimensions of this volume the author has not been able to do more than describe the processes most generally used in the trade at the present time, but this should enable the reader to arrive more quickly at the essential information he requires.

CONTENTS

LIST OF ILLUSTRATIONS

CHAPTER I

GENERAL CONSIDERATIONS AND REQUIREMENTS

SECTION 1. BRIEF OUTLINE OF THE PROCESS

THE application of photography to lithography has been proceeding apace for a number of years and has now reached the stage where "photo-litho," as it is generally termed, is not merely a minor branch of reproduction work but a craft or process exclusively employed or taking precedence in all modern lithographic houses.

The old method of preparing metal press plates by drawing direct or transferring is now almost entirely superseded by photo-mechanical methods which reproduce every detail of the copy and in correct tonal value. The process is not of course entirely mechanical, the final results depending on the skill and experience of the operators and artists employed in the several stages. The general procedure is briefly summarized as follows—

The original to be reproduced is placed on the copy-board of a specially constructed camera and illuminated usually by powerful arc lamps. The image is focused to the correct size and a negative made which in the case of a line subject would consist of perfectly clear lines on an opaque ground. If the original is a "continuous-tone" subject such as a water-colour sketch, wash drawing or an ordinary photographic print, the photographic image has to be split up into dots of equal density but varying in size corresponding to the tones of the copy. This is accomplished by placing a "half-tone screen" at a specific distance in front, or in the case of "contact screens," immediately in contact with the sensitive plate.

For colour work an appropriate colour-separated negative is made for each of the colour printings. These negatives must be hand corrected by the artist.

The grained litho plate which is to receive the photographic impression is thoroughly and chemically cleaned and coated with a light-sensitive albumen solution. A special whirling and drying machine is employed to spread and dry the coating evenly. The plate with the negative in the required position is placed in a vacuum frame which in operation firmly presses the negative film into close contact with the plate surface. The surrounding area of the plate is protected from light, usually by roller-blinds attached to the frame, and then an exposure made to powerful arc lamps. This renders the sensitive albumen coating immediately beneath the clear portions of the film insoluble in cold water.

The whole surface of the plate is coated with a thin film of tenacious ink similar to a combination of litho and transfer ink. Immersion in cold water permits the washing away of all portions of the albumen film which have been protected from the action of light by the opaque portions of the negative, leaving on the plate an extremely strong and perfectly sharp dual image consisting of a hardened albumen base with an acid-resisting ink surface.

A modified litho procedure follows which results in a plate ready for immediate printing on the press.

At the time of writing the Fourth Edition, the more recently perfected "deep etch" plate and "bimetal" photo-litho plate, are accepted procedures. These latter processes consist of printing down from a "positive"; the resulting light-hardened coating representing the non-printing portions acts as a resist during a very slight etch of the metal, or removal of the surface layer in a bimetal process.

In "Deep Etch," the plate surface is treated with a "litho

base" or greasy ink, before the light-hardened stencil is removed. The exposed lower layer of a bimetal plate is usually ink- or water-receptive, by contrast to the protected metal layer and thereby acts as a lithographic image on the printing press. These processes are more costly to operate but considerable advantages exist in both the photographic work and printing on the machine.

Special equipment is available for duplicate and group printing of negatives on the plate. Such equipment is essential for modern requirements of colour reproduction where several plates have to be prepared in perfect register.

SECTION 2. SELECTION OF EQUIPMENT

A list of the necessary items of equipment for an average initial plant is given on pages 8 to 12. This list must be modified according to individual requirements. The selection of equipment is a matter upon which the services of an experienced man should be obtained if possible, for the questions of economy, efficiency, maximum size, quantity and class of contemplated output, proposed staff, financial and other limitations, probable future extensions, etc., must all be given careful consideration. Reputable supply houses are always willing to send a fully competent representative to discuss and advise on these matters, his advice being based on years of intimate association with the trade and a thorough knowledge of its requirements.

The equipment to be installed having been decided on, the layout of the department should also be left in the hands of an expert, but a few remarks on the subject may be of use here. The total number of rooms in the department will again depend on individual circumstances, but assuming an artists' room, camera studio and metal-printing room, all of adequate dimensions, these should be arranged to permit of the natural sequence of procedure from work on the original to despatch of the finished plate.

The artists' room should be provided with wide benches so positioned that the maximum advantage is obtained of all available daylight both for working up original sketches, photographs, etc., and illumination of the copy when negatives are being retouched on the retouching desks. Part of this room may be partitioned off as an office if this is desirable.

The photgraphic studio will be apportioned to camera room, dark-rooms, store room, and glass-cleaning room as space permits. The camera room must be of sufficient size to allow ample working space around the camera stand, and if a prism is included allowance must be made for the position of the camera, copyboard and lamps when making reversed negatives. When employing the "behind-copyboard" type of transparency attachment it is necessary to allow space at the rear of the stand for arc lamps and reflector. Space should also be available for a copy table with cupboards for screens, lenses, etc. The stripping table and sink should preferably be in a partitioned corner of the room. Strong illumination is not necessary nor advisable for the camera, and if possible windows and general lighting should not be immediately behind the focusing screen.

While modern camera stands are constructed to nullify the effect of average floor vibration, it is advisable to have the whole department in a part of the building where vibration does not occur or is at a minimum.

While it is possible to use only one dark-room such economy of space is extremely ill-advised. Two rooms at least should be constructed, one for the wet collodion process and the other for working with dry plates, bromide paper, etc. Usually the former is the larger room, but ample space should be allowed in the dry-plate room for accommodating a special contact printing frame of the box pattern. When planning these rooms the entrances should be arranged to be as near as possible to the camera end of the stand. More recently designed cameras are made to be built into the dark-room wall, thereby reducing operators' walking to a minimum. Sliding light-proof doors are preferable to the ordinary swinging type, both on account of taking up less space and their minimum disturbance of floor dust. Smooth walls and floor covering and rounded corners throughout also assist in the elimination of the frequent trouble caused by dust. Thorough ventilation through light-traps, and independent control of temperature for the dark-rooms, are essential. Large lead-lined or slate sinks, with draining boards and benches, are arranged in the most convenient positions leaving generous working space. Shelves above the benches and cupboards below should be constructed for stock solutions and utensils. A separate store room should be used for dry chemicals and general supplies.

The water supply to each sink should be controlled by a side tap and fed through a swinging arm to the end of which is attached about two feet of flexible tube. This applies to all sinks in the department.

A sufficient number of dark-room lamps must be constructed or purchased to give a full but "safe" illumination. It must be remembered, however, that no light is entirely safe, and consequently the lamps must be so arranged that no direct rays fall on a sensitive plate for any length of time, or better still, not at all.

White light for general illumination of the dark-rooms should be controlled by switches placed away from the doors to avoid inadvertent fogging of the plates. If the switches are already in position and grouped, a length of thin chain or cord could be attached to the switch controlling a yellow light.

The interior of a dark-room is usually painted a depressingly dull grey, red or black. Excepting special cases where such apparatus as step and repeat projection machines are employed, this is entirely unnecessary. It also leads to the probable use of a dark-room lamp of too high an intensity, with the consequent possibility of plate fog. If the dark-room is painted a light buff or similar bright colour, operating conditions are obviously more cheerful and conducive to more efficient work, and a reasonable working light is obtained over the whole room with the minimum intensity of light source. The light reflected from the walls is, of course, only that emitted by the orange or red dark-room lamp, and consequently even if white enamel is used there is no increased danger of fog.

A very beneficial refinement for the wet collodion process is the inclusion of a separate dark-room for coating and sensitizing the plates. This could be connected to both the main dark-room and the camera room, and with the view of maintaining absolute cleanliness should have only the bench for the silver bath and draining pads, a shelf for the collodion and glass plates ready for immediate use, and a small shelf at a convenient height to accommodate the dark-slide.

If space is very limited the glass-cleaning will have to be done in the general dark-room, but if possible a separate dust-proof room with a sink and drying racks should be provided. An electric temperature-controlled drying cabinet is useful for the quick drying of prepared glass or negatives. Again, if space permits, it is highly desirable to fit a sink in an open and well-ventilated position for all such manipulations as the final blackening of wet collodion negatives, the fumes from the sodium or ammonium sulphide which is used being detrimental to good work.

The "printing-down" room should be adjacent to the studio and will have to accommodate one or preferably two lead-lined sinks a few inches larger than the maximum size of machine plate, a whirling and drying machine, a vacuum frame with arc lamps, a rolling-up bench, and ink table or deep-etch developing table fitted with cutters. Ample working and bench space must be allowed, and also cupboards for metal storage.

These should be in a position where the plates will be kept absolutely dry at all times. The lighting of the room can be of light yellow. It is quite unnecessary deliberately to cut out any available daylight; the windows could be of suitable coloured glass or covered with yellow fabric. Roller blinds with side boards are an advantage, in that full white light is then available when desired, such as during plate development in the sink. In this connexion it is recommended that the sink be positioned in front of a window. If a large amount of work is likely to be passing through this department it would be advisable to have a separate room and sink for developing purposes, and so arranged that the best possible light is thrown on the plate for thorough examination of the plate and image. The sink should be open on at least two sides and a powerful adjustable lamp fitted with an opaque shade suspended in a convenient position. A hand lamp with flexible lead is a useful accessory, particularly in connexion with the ordinary vacuum frame, near which the necessary electric point would be included. Electric lights over working positions such as sinks and benches in the whole department should be fitted with adjustable counterweights.

Sinks should have loose-fitting wood grids constructed of, say, $2\frac{1}{2}$ in. $\times$ 1 in. battens, with spaces of about 1 in.

SECTION 3. LIST OF EQUIPMENT

With the view of avoiding the consequent confusion of too many alternative methods and suggestions in the following instructions it will generally be assumed that the installation consists of the following apparatus and sundries. This list may be taken as a guide for the selection of equipment, and is representative of the average initial plant for the production of commercial work in line and screen for black and white and colour, and employing wet collodion, dry plate, film and paper.

1 Screen Camera, 20 in. × 24 in.

1 All-metal Spring Stand of sufficient length to permit of 4½–5 diameters reduction.

1 25 in. or 30 in. Lens.

1 Prism for same.

1 Diaphragm Indicator and Spring Tape Scale.

1 Set of Half-tone Stops.

1 Set of Colour Filters cemented in optical flats.

1 Filter Holder and Preserving Box.

1 All-metal Transparency Attachment.

1 20 in. × 24 in. Glass-fronted Copy Holder.

1 Paper and Film Negative Holder for attachment to dark-slide.

1 Focusing Eye-piece.

1 Focusing Cloth.

1 Set of three Original Engraved Half-tone Screens, ruled at angles of 45°, 75° and 90°—133 lines per inch, *or* 1 Circular Screen and Holder.

1 Set of Four-Point Arc Lamps comprising four single arc lamps suspended from the camera stand lamp supports.

1 24 in. × 30 in. Shining-up Table (stripping table).

1 Retouching Desk.

1 Aerograph Equipment.

1 Quad Demy Enclosed and Electrically Heated Whirler with variable speed control and water supply fitted.

1 Quad Demy All-metal Face-up Vacuum Frame with motor exhaust equipment.

2 Printing Type Arc Lamps on tripod stands.

1 20 in. × 24 in. Vacuum Printing Cabinet for contact negatives.

3 Dark-room Lamps.

3 Orange Safe-lights.

1 Ruby Safe-light.

1 Green Safe-light suitable for panchromatic plate work.

2 Dark-room Clocks.

1 Negative Drying Rack 24 in. × 20 in., or Drying Cabinet.

1 Negative Drying Rack 15 in. × 12 in.

2 Negative Drying Racks 12 in. × 10 in.

1 20 in . × 16 in. Grooved Glass-soaking Trough.

3 One-gallon Silver-bath Bottles.

1 Argentometer and Tube.

1 Evaporating Basin and Sand Bath.

1 Heavy Pattern Silver Bath Hook.
1 16-oz Collodion Pouring Bottle.
2 Pneumatic Plate Holders.
2 4 in. Camel Hair Negative Dusting Brushes.
1 Glass Cleaning Vice.
1 Electric Fan or Blower.
4 Glass Cleaning Brushes.
1 Set of Grain Scales and Weights.
1 Set of Chemical Scales and Weights.
1 15 in. × 12 in. Bromide Printing Frame.
1 Gas Ring or Electric Hot Plate.
1 6 in. Pestle and Mortar.
3 26 in. × 22 in. Porcelain Dishes ⎫
2 20 in. × 16 in. Porcelain Dishes ⎬ or suitable non-corrosion
3 16 in. × 14 in. Porcelain Dishes ⎪ plastic dishes.
3 13 in. × 11 in. Porcelain Dishes ⎭
2 32-oz Glass Measures.
2 20-oz Glass Measures.
4 10-oz Glass Measures.
2 4-oz Glass Measures conical.
2 10-oz Celluloid Beakers.
2 10 in. Glass Funnels.
2 6 in. Glass Funnels.
2 3 in. Glass Funnels.
2 6 in. Enamelled Iron Funnels.
Selection of Spotting Brushes.
1 Ruling Pen.
1 12 in. Celluloid Rule.
1 12 in. Nickelled-steel Rule.
1 36 in. Nickelled-steel Rule.
1 Register Gauge.
2 Artists' Erasing Knives.
1 Oil Stone.
1 Box of Drawing Pins.
1 Diamond Glass Cutter.
2 6 in. Flat Squeegees.
3 Chamois Leathers.
2 Selvyt Cloths.
2 doz Glass Stirring Rods.
1 Thermometer.

1 Hand Lamp, Extension and Guard.
1 12 in. Fine Nap Roller with Leather Hand Grips.
1 20 in. × 15 in. (approx.) Litho Stone.
1 6 in. Palette Knife.
1 3 in. Push Knife.
12 Selected Sponges.
1 Large Linen-tester.
12 Ink Erasers.
Selection of empty bottles.
Supply of suitable Carbons for the arc lamps.

CHEMICALS

The quantities suggested below must only be taken as a rough guide for the commencement of a department and its operation for a limited period.

1 Winchester Pure Glacial Acetic Acid.
1 lb Citric Acid Crystals.
1 Winchester Pure Hydrochloric Acid.
1 Winchester Commercial Nitric Acid.
1 pint Pure Nitric Acid.
1 pint Phosphoric Acid.
½ lb Jar Aerowhite.
5 lb Albumen Crystals.
7 lb Alum, powdered.
1 Winchester Ammonia, 0·880.
8 oz Amidol.
2 lb Ammonium Bichromate, extra pure.
1 lb Ammonium Biphosphate.
1 lb Ammonium Nitrate.
2 lb Bitumen Powder.
1 ream White Blotting Paper, Photo quality.
2 Winchesters Collodion and Iodizer.
1 pint Collodion Thinning Solution.
7 lb Copper Sulphate, crushed.
2 lb Cotton Wool, best quality.
2 gallons Distilled Water.
1 lb Formaline.
5 lb French Chalk.
2 32-oz Bottles Fish Glue.
1 lb Glycerine.

7 lb Gum Arabic.
14 lb Hypo.
1 lb India Rubber Solution.
1 lb Iodine, resublimed.
1 Winchester Iron Perchloride Solution.
7 lb Iron Sulphate.
1 ream Josef Paper.
1 lb Lead Nitrate.
2 pints Litho Plate Etch (Atzol, Litholene, etc.).
12 Sticks Litho Writing Ink.
4 boxes Litho Crayons.
12 books Litmus Paper, Blue.
1 lb Mercury Bichloride.
8 oz Metol.
1 gallon Methylated Spirit.
8 oz Methyl Violet.
Supply of Negative Glass, according to requirements, say—
2 doz 8½ in. × 6½ in.
2 doz 10 in. × 8 in.
2 doz 12 in. × 10 in.
1 doz 15 in. × 12 in.
1 doz 20 in. × 16 in.
1 doz 24 in. × 20 in.
10 oz Photopake.
1 lb Photo-Litho Ink.
1 lb Potassium Bromide.
5 lb Potassium Carbonate.
7 lb Potassium Caustic, cleaning.
2 lb Potassium Hydrate, pure sticks.
7 lb Potassium Cyanide.
1 lb Potassium Ferricyanide.
2 lb Potassium Iodide.
1 lb Potassium Metabisulphite.
1 lb Potassium Permanganate.
2 pots Process Black.
2 lb Russian Tallow.
2 lb Silver Nitrate.
7 lb Sodium Carbonate.
7 lb Sodium Sulphide.
7 lb Sodium Sulphite.

1 lb Sodium Fluoride.
2 lb Tin Foil, extra thin.
2 pints Turpentine, pure.
2 pints Hard Negative Varnish.
2 pints Matt Varnish.
2 pints Washout Solution.
1 pint Vandyke Ink.
Supply of Rags.

When the fitting of the department is completed and the full supply of chemicals and utensils obtained, all the rooms together with benches, shelves and equipment must be thoroughly cleaned and every precaution taken against the future accumulation of dust. The importance of cleanliness and ventilation is always emphasized by writers and instructors on the wet collodion process—and justly so, for strict attention to these points results in a very real saving of time and money. However, it is an unfortunate fact that rarely does one come across a department which has been in operation for any length of time conforming to the standard of cleanliness insisted upon at the commencement. The trouble appears to be that it is nobody's job to attend to such work at the proper time. Operators will not allow sweeping or anything but a superficial tidying while the normal work of the studio is being undertaken. At the end of the day the regular shop cleaners are naturally not encouraged to be "let loose" amongst chemicals and easily broken negatives. It should be realized by managers of departments that both time and materials would be saved if, say, ten minutes before closing time each day were allotted to supervised cleaning. Temporary rush of work and overtime might result in avoidance of such regulations unless orders are rigorously enforced. Two or three occasions of neglect are often quite sufficient to establish a general laxity upon which follows so much trouble. So long as work is being turned out conditions are allowed to pass which get one degree worse week by week, but quite unnecessary time is spent in correcting faults which should never have occurred; negatives are produced which require an excessive amount of spotting, others are beyond repair and have to be re-made, chemicals are wasted and the silver bath requires purifying long before it should be necessary. These losses are not always apparent, as everyone appears to be engaged on necessary work, and the week's output when dealing with average photo-litho work is frequently difficult to compare with that of the previous week or with a similar period a month or so previously.

Another general note which is more applicable to a new department staffed by men of average experience: So much has been said and written during the past few years about photo-litho and all its possibilities that firms embarking on this process are quite naturally but rather unduly impatient to see results which are really beyond reasonable expectations when dealing with a newly engaged staff. The principals immediately want to see first-class reproductions of difficult subjects, or intricate combination jobs, and these, most probably, to be printed by machine minders having no experience of photographically-prepared plates. The staff, anxious to demonstrate the capabilities of the process, are chary of raising objections when such work is proposed as a trial, and then, simply because the department as a whole is not "worked in" nor the very necessary co-operation established between this and other departments, the results are disappointing; certainly not so good as they would be a little later when the several persons concerned in the reproduction have had opportunities to feel their way and work together. Surely it is only natural to start at the beginning and make certain that each stage in any such process or craft as photo-litho is carried through satisfactorily and with assurance before commencing the next?

CHAPTER II

STUDIO PREPARATIONS

SECTION 1. WEIGHTS AND MEASURES

BRITISH weights and measures are frequently a source of confusion, and when collecting formulae from various sources the student will probably have to deal with apothecaries' weight, avoirdupois weight and metric weights and measures. With regard to the English weights, trouble can often be minimized by remembering that the grain is the common unit.

Apothecaries' Weight—

    20 grains   = 1 scruple.
    3 scruples = 1 drachm.
    8 drachms = 1 ounce (oz) = 480 grains.

Avoirdupois Weight (generally employed)—

    $437\frac{1}{2}$ grains = 1 ounce (28·35 grammes).
    16 ounces   = 1 pound (lb) = 7000 grains = 0·454 kilogramme.
    $\frac{1}{4}$ ounce   = 109 grains.
    $\frac{1}{2}$ ounce   = 219 grains.

Fluid Measure—

    60 minims = 1 dram   =   3·55 c.c.
    8 drams   = 1 ounce = 480 minims = 28·4 c.c.
    20 ounces = 1 pint   = 568   c.c.
    2 pints   = 1 quart   = 1·136 litres.
    4 quarts   = 1 gallon = 160 ounces = 4·546 litres.

NOTE.—1 fluid ounce of water weighs 437·5 grains = 28·35 grammes.

Metric Weights and Measures

The unit of weight is the gramme (g) and while there are names for subdivisions and multiples, it is customary to employ the terms 0·1, 0·01, 10 or 100 g, etc. The following are a few useful approximate equivalents—

Linear Measure—

1 millimetre (mm)	= 0·03937 inch.
1 centimetre (cm)	= 0·3937 inch.
1 metre (m)	= 39·37 inches
	(1 inch = 2·54 cm).

Weight—

1 milligramme $(\frac{1}{1000}$ g)	= 0·015 grain.
1 gramme	= 15·432 grains.
1 kilogramme (1000 g)	= 35·27 ounces = 2·2 lb.

Fluid Measure—

1 cubic centimetre (c.c.)	= 16·9 minims.
1 litre (l)	= 35 oz 94 minims.

A convenient method of expressing certain formulae is by means of the word "parts," and this should be properly understood. A formula consisting of "parts" of solids and liquids implies grains for the solid and minims for the liquid, or ounces and fluid ounces, or grammes and cubic centimetres.

Percentage solutions are often not completely understood: when, say, a 20 per cent solution is to be made it means that each 100 parts of *completed solution* includes 20 parts of chemical. To make up a 25 per cent solution of hypo, for each 40 oz of finished solution 10 oz of hypo would be required. This is placed in the measure and water added to a total of 40 oz. It will be noted that for practical purposes a completed solution is measured by volume, not by weight; although, of course, the solids are weighed out in the first place.

The majority of photographic formulae are not extremely critical so far as quantity is concerned, but it is at all times important to follow instructions correctly when these are definitely stated, and a full understanding of the foregoing is essential, especially so when dealing with high-percentage solutions. A useful reminder for the beginner is the obvious connexion between a 50 per cent solution and the idiomatic phrase "fifty-fifty"—equal parts of each.

SECTION 2. PREPARATION OF STOCK SOLUTIONS

A selection of wide-mouth bottles of approximately 16-oz capacity, and of different shapes, should be provided as pouring bottles for the solutions which are in constant use. If such bottles were all identical it might frequently lead to error when working in subdued light. The majority of stock solutions are kept in "Winchesters," which are of about 80 fluid oz capacity.

The following are made up as a commencement—

Solution No. 1. Glass-cleaning Solution

To each gallon (6 litres) of water in the soaking trough add 30 oz (1·125 litres) commercial nitric acid or acetic acid.

Solution No. 2. Albumen Substratum

Egg albumen .	.	.	$1\frac{1}{2}$ oz	or	20 g
Water up to .	.	.	80 oz		1000 c.c.
Liq. ammonia .	.	.	$\frac{1}{4}$ oz		3 c.c.

Alternatively—

The whites of two eggs.					
Water .	.	.	80 oz	or	1 litre
Liq. ammonia .	.	.	1 dram		1·5 c.c.

Collodion

It is not recommended that the novice attempts to make up his own collodion and iodizer, as this might lead to trouble which would be difficult to locate. It is better obtained from specializing manufacturers who usually supply it in two bottles, one containing plain collodion and the other the iodizing solution. These are in the correct proportions of three parts of the former to one part of the latter. The iodized collodion should be allowed to stand for about 24 hours before use. It is sometimes recommended to filter collodion before use, but modern manufacturing methods including prolonged standing and decantation render this precaution unnecessary.

NOTE. Those wishing to make up their own collodion will find the following quite satisfactory for both line and screen work—

Collodion

Celloidin (or equivalent)	.	1 oz			28 g
Ether 0·720	. .	60 oz	} or {	1700 c.c.
Pure alcohol 0·835	.	40 oz			1140 c.c.

Iodizer

Alcohol 0·805 .	.	10 oz			284 c.c.
Cadmium iodide	.	240 gr			16 g
Amm. iodide .	.	180 gr			12 g
Cadmium bromide .	.	15 gr	} or {	1 g
Calcium chloride	.	30 gr			2 g
Iodide, resublimed .	.	10 gr			0·6 g

Solution No. 3. Silver Bath

Transparent white bottles of adequate capacity are required for this solution. At least two baths should be made up, for while one is in use the other can be standing in daylight to assist the precipitation of impurities. The silver bath consists of 35 gr (2 g) of silver nitrate in each ounce (25 c.c.) of solution, therefore for an 80 oz bath slightly over 6¼ oz of silver nitrate will be required. A stronger bath of about 40 grains to the ounce is frequently advised for screen work. The solution must be slightly acid: make up a solution of ¼ oz (8 c.c.) acetic acid, ¼ oz (8 c.c) pure nitric acid, and 1 oz (32 c.c.) water. Slowly add sufficient of this to the bath to turn blue litmus paper red. The argentometer which gives a reading of grains of silver nitrate per ounce of solution can be used to test the strength of the solution. In the case of continental argentometers the reading is in grammes per 100 c.c. (The solution should contain 8 g per 100 c.c.) With an old bath in which a certain amount of impurities has been deposited the reading will not be an absolutely true indication of the silver content; an estimated allowance must be made.

Before use the solution must be thoroughly filtered. For this purpose one of the large 10-in. funnels is used and kept exclusively for silver. A wad of cotton-wool is forced into the neck of the funnel. This will only allow the solution to filter through very slowly, so plenty of time must be allowed. A few ounces should be filtered through and then poured back into the funnel. This is to get rid of any loose particles of cotton which might be freed from the wad and would otherwise be retained in the filtered solution. The silver-bath bottles must be absolutely clean, and after washing should preferably be rinsed out with distilled water. If the use of tap-water is unavoidable the solution must be stood in daylight for a day or two before filtering.

Solution No. 4. Iron Developer

Iron sulphate	.	.	. 4 oz		100 g
Pure glacial acetic acid		.	4 oz	or	100 c.c.
Alcohol	.	.	. 2 oz		50 c.c.
Water up to	.	.	. 80 oz		2000 c.c.

Industrial spirit is frequently used in practice in place of pure alcohol. If desired, a saturated solution of iron may be made up and kept in good condition by the addition of sufficient pure sulphuric acid to prevent the solution from going "rusty." For use, dilute to a hydrometer reading of 4° Bé. The iron sulphate should be of bright green appearance, and must be kept in an air-tight container. Lack of this precaution results in oxidization and is indicated by the crystals turning brown. The amount of acid and alcohol in the developer depends on circumstances which will be described later. The solution must be kept in a well-stoppered bottle, and not used if discoloration has commenced.

Solution No. 5. Fixing Solution

Potassium cyanide	.	. 2 oz	or	50 g
Water	. . .	. 40 oz		1000 c.c.

This formula assumes cyanide of about 98 per cent. Owing to the extremely poisonous nature of this salt every possible care must be taken, and the bottles conspicuously labelled "Poison." The worker must also endeavour to avoid inhaling the fumes when employing the solution.

Solution No. 6. Ferricyanide Stock Solution

Potassium ferricyanide	. 2 oz	or	50 g
Water up to	. . . 20 oz		500 c.c.

Solution No. 7. Lead Intensifier

Lead nitrate	. .	. 2 oz		50 g
Pot. ferricyanide	.	. 2 oz	or	50 g
Pure glacial acetic acid	.	2 oz		50 c.c.
Water up to	. .	. 40 oz		1000 c.c.

Filter and keep in the dark-room; preferably use a brown bottle.

Solution No. 8. Copper Intensifier

Copper sulphate	.	. 4 oz		100 g
Pot. bromide	. .	. 2 oz	or	50 g
Water up to	. .	. 40 oz		1000 c.c.

This should be allowed to stand for a period before use.

Solution No. 9. Blackening Silver

Silver nitrate	.	.	. 4 oz	160 g
Citric acid	.	.	. ½ oz	20 g
Nitric acid	.	.	. ¼ oz	10 c.c.
Water up to	.	.	. 40 oz	1600 c.c.

with "or" bracketing the two columns.

Solution No. 10. Iodine Intensifier

Pot. iodide	.	.	. 4 oz	100 g
Iodine, resublimed	.	.	2 oz	50 g
Water up to	.	.	. 80 oz	2000 c.c.

Solution No. 11. Final Blackening Solution

Sodium sulphide	.	. 1 oz	50 g
Water	.	. . 20 oz	1000 c.c.

The sulphide crystals must be kept in an air-tight bottle, and the solution away from the dark-room whenever possible. The strength of the solution is not critical and it is advised that the estimated quantity of crystals is placed straight in the stock bottle without measuring on the scales. Owing to the deliquescent nature of sodium sulphide it will sometimes be found that a portion of the crystals has turned to liquid; this must not be used, and may be washed away by a short rinse of the crystals before dissolving.

Solution No. 12. Gum Solution

Gum arabic	.	. . 4 oz	100 g
Hot water	.	. . 40 oz	1000 c.c.

When dissolved add a few drops of preservative such as carbolic acid or thymol, and thoroughly filter. Do not cork the bottle but keep in a dust-free position or use a piece of smooth paper and a rubber band.

SECTION 3. SETTING UP THE CAMERA

To obtain a fair estimate of the alignment and squareness of the camera, place a straight-edge on the front mount of the lens and projecting beyond the side of the front body. With a suitable rod, measure the distance from the straight-edge to the rear of the back body. Repeat the measurement at the opposite side and the top. All three of these distances should coincide. It might be found with an old camera, particularly if it has been roughly handled, that the two bodies have spread a little at the top. This can be remedied by slackening the bolts holding the frame of one of the bodies to its baseboard and inserting a narrow strip of thin card between the two in such a manner as to bring the two bodies into alignment again. Now check the plane of the copy-board in relation to the focusing screen or rear of the back body by measuring the distance between each corner of the rear face and the opposing corner of the copy-board. To facilitate such measurements a small projecting nail at one end of a suitable rod may be allowed to bear on the rear face and the camera adjusted until the opposite end of the rod just touches the copy-board. Any variation between the top and bottom corners can be corrected by an adjusting device which is usually at the bottom of the copy-board. Lateral correction is effected by adjusting the stops for the camera turn-table. Special apparatus is used by the camera suppliers to ensure that new cameras are in correct adjustment, and a higher degree of accuracy is assured than is detectable by the normal photographic means.

When the camera has a wood base resting on a metal carriage, it is important to see that the two are bolted together after erection. This is a point which often gets missed and results in the camera getting out of alignment with consequent distortion of the image.

The screen gear must be tested for parallelism with the

THE "H P" ARC GEAR CAMERA

focusing screen: nuts and springs or similar devices are provided for this purpose. Remove the shutter from the dark-slide, and with the latter on the camera operate the screen gear until the plate-holding bars or "plate sticks" are just touching the "screen sticks." This might occur at one point only. Make adjustments

THE "H.P." ARC GEAR CAMERA AND "DOMINION" ALL-METAL
CAMERA STAND

on the four corner nuts until both pairs of opposing sticks are just touching throughout their length.

While making these adjustments attention must be given to the agreement of the scale reading with the distance between the bearing surfaces of the stops on the plate sticks and those of the screen sticks. If only one screen is to be used (or all screens are of the same thickness) the scale may be adjusted to give a reading to the actual screen rulings, thus obviating the necessity of making the usual allowance for the thickness of the cover glass.

The registration of the dark-slide with the focusing screen of an old camera must be carefully checked. Detach the bellows from the rear body. Place the dark-slide containing a flat sheet of glass in position. Bring the screen gear forward against a definite stop, insert a wedge between the sticks and the glass, and mark the wedge at its limit of entrance. Replace the dark-slide with the focusing screen, and if this is correct the wedge

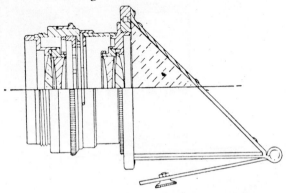

DIAGRAM OF COOKE PROCESS LENS AND PRISM

showing arrangement of the two lens combinations each consisting of a Double Concave and a Double Convex Lens at exact separations. The main function of the prism itself is to protect the silver reflecting surface without causing duplication or distortion of the image.

should enter between the screen sticks and focusing screen to the same extent. A slip of paper can be used for the same purpose. This should just be gripped by the glass in the dark-slide and the glass in the focusing screen with the screen sticks in a constant position. If errors are noticed, the seating of the focusing screen will have to be planed down or packed as required.

The "Process Lens" employed is of special design to meet the requirements of photo mechanical work. The image of a near subject such as a flat drawing or photograph perpendicular to the lens axis must be rendered sharp and practically flat. All of the several colour images must be in exact register and of equal definition.

The lens must be free from astigmatism—that is, all lines both vertical and horizontal must be equally sharp. An iris diaphragm should be fitted and a slot provided for Waterhouse Stops.

LOW MODEL ALL-METAL CAMERA STAND
(Note easy access to all parts of camera)

The diagonal of the rectangle it is desired to cover with object and image same size is usually taken as a guide for the size of lens to be selected. For a 15 in. × 12 in. camera an 18-in. focal length lens is suitable, or for a 20 in. × 20 in. camera a 25-in. lens. If a reversing prism is likely to be required, this is preferably ordered at the same time as the lens. This also necessitates exact manufacture throughout to maintain the high standard of definition in line or colour half-tone demanded of modern optical equipment.

The majority of camera stands are supported by some type

of spring suspension, or vibration-absorbing mounting such as rubber and steel bonding, to minimize the effects of floor vibration. Any movement of one end of the camera is thus simultaneously transmitted to the other, consequently the camera

THE "H.P." DIAPHRAGM INDICATOR

and copy-board remain relatively stationary. The advantages of this arrangement must not be over-estimated, however, and if the camera has been rocked it should be steadied as far as possible before commencing an exposure.

Cameras which are constructed on floor rails may only be installed in a room which is entirely free from vibration, such an area of floor being isolated from any other part of the floor by an earth channel not less than 9 in. wide all round.

In the list of apparatus a Diaphragm Indicator and Scale were included. There are several arrangements available for the purpose for which this is intended: they vary both in elaboration and price, and it is also possible to construct a simple scaling device without any expenditure beyond that of a little time. The first object of all these systems is to provide an aid towards standardization of methods and results by indicating the correct size of stop to use with any camera extension. This is of particular importance when dealing with screen work, and the subject will be discussed in detail later in the appropriate chapter.

For the present purpose it will be assumed that the lens is fitted with a radial diaphragm indicator and a spring tape and pointer at the side of the camera. The former indicates the actual diameter of the iris diaphragm in fractions of an inch, and the latter the extension of the camera in inches. For practical purposes the extension is taken as being the distance between the lens stop and the focusing screen. (When using the metric system the diaphragm indicator is calibrated in millimetres and the spring tape in divisions of 64 millimetres, and numbered accordingly.)

Copy-board Illumination

The use of "four-point" open type arc lamps has become universal practice on account of their excellent covering capacity together with intense illumination and economical consumption of electricity: the four lamps can be run in series on, say, a 200 volts supply with little consequent dissipation of current by the resistances. These lamps are particularly useful when dealing with large subjects which are so common in photo-lithography. A copy the full size of the board can be evenly illuminated at a distance very much less than is necessary with only one lamp at each side. If it is required to cover a large copy with only two lamps they will have to be positioned at a comparatively great distance, which will, of course, cut down the intensity of illumination and increase the exposure time considerably. Illumination varies inversely as the square of the distance from its source: for instance, if a lamp at a normal distance of three feet allows an exposure of, say, 30 sec, and the lamps were then repositioned at 6 ft the necessary exposure

THE EMPIRE ARC LIGHTING UNIT FOR COPY-BOARD ILLUMINATION

would be two minutes, not twice the amount as might at first be expected. (See page 33.)

The use of open type arc lamps is essential for the production of economical and good work on account of the superior colour separation obtained and consequent reduced hand correction on the negatives.

Daylight illumination can only be used satisfactorily in suitable climates where the intensity and actinic value remain reasonably constant from day to day, and hourly variations can be tabulated. We believe there are few places where photographic conditions remain effectively constant the whole year round, and it would

HAND-OPERATED CAMERA, SHOWING DARK-ROOM CONTROLS

always be wise therefore to have a set of lamps available for irregular periods and night work. When daylight is used the arrangements should allow for an even flood of light with no direct rays of sunlight falling on or near the camera. Suitable reflectors such as whitened walls can be employed where existing rooms have to be used to the best advantage.

Special Equipment for Large Negatives

Generally speaking, the standard type of reproduction camera does not exceed 30 in. × 40 in. in size: for work beyond this

ADAPTERS FOR ARC GEAR CAMERA

Projection Type

The largest screen the camera will take can be used on this type of adapter, as the plate is advanced to the screen in correct register.

Plain Type

In this type the screen is moved towards the negative, and can only be used when the screen is small enough to come into the small dark slide. This adapter is advantageous for line and continuous tone copying, simply removing screen from camera.

size dark-room cameras are usually constructed. One form of dark-room camera has the lens board fitted to the dark-room wall by a short bellows extension, with a travelling copy holder on rails in the studio and a travelling plate holder and screen mechanism, also designed to hold the focusing screen, moving

EBONITE SILVER BATH CONTAINER ON STAND

on floor rails or overhead rails (for safety) inside the dark-room. The other more modern form is the highly developed apparatus having the "backbody" or "camera back" fitted in the dark-room wall. This has a space saving effect and permits all the controls to the front of the camera and the copy-board to be operated at a position adjacent to the focusing screen. Such apparatus saves endless time, operates with absolute precision and safety and enables large screens to be brought into use without fear of damage. Dark-slides are, of course, not required.

Such equipments as the above are usually constructed to suit the user's special requirements and may include apparatus for the use of large rolls of negative paper, and quick-change copy holders for book reprints, etc.

Porcelain dishes for the silver bath are not obtainable beyond certain sizes, and a special container has to be used. This may consist of a wooden trough lined with suitable material, or a specially constructed ebonite container resting in a wood outer casing, the whole supported on a stand as illustrated.

The standard camera in sizes from, say, 24 in. × 24 in. upwards, is mostly supplied with an adapter consisting of an adapter frame, focusing screen and dark-slide of about 15 in. × 12 in. In the average commercial house employing large cameras a great proportion of the work is on comparatively small plates and the use of an adapter obviates the necessity of continually working with the heavy dark-slide. There are two general arrangements: one, the plain type, requires the use of a half-tone screen which is small enough to enter the front of the dark-slide. Short projecting screen sticks which can be attached to the permanent screen sticks must be supplied. The other type of adapter is known as the projector, and enables the full-size screen to be used with either dark-slide. With this frame the small focusing screen is brought to the same plane as the large screen, and the dark-slide is specially constructed to enable the plate to be brought forward the required distance after opening the roller shutter.

CHAPTER III

STUDIO WORK—WET COLLODION

SECTION 1. COMMENCING WORK

THE first subject should be a fairly broad line sketch or page of type matter. This is placed in the centre of the copy-board either by pinning or using one of the several types of glass-fronted copy holders. The former method is very troublesome when dealing with thin or creased paper. The copy holder is much preferable as it prevents copies being damaged by pins and holds them perfectly flat when otherwise the heat of the arc lamps would probably curl them. The position of the lamps is very important and two or three positions should definitely be decided upon—this to assist standardization of exposure and working speed. When using the four-point lamps it will probably be found that two positions will suffice, one at, say, 30 in. for copies of 20 in. $\times$ 16 in. and under, and one at 42 in. for the maximum size of copy contemplated down to 20 in. $\times$ 16 in. With the latter distance the exposure will be doubled.

If additional lamp distances are employed, the relative exposures can be ascertained from the formula—

$$\text{Multiplying factor} = \frac{\text{New distance}^2}{\text{Normal distance}^2}$$

Example. New distance 52 in., normal distance 30 in.

$$\frac{52^2}{30^2} = \frac{2704}{900} = 3$$

The normal exposure will therefore be multiplied by three.

Measure lamp distances from the centre of copy to the carbons. The angle at which the light falls on the copy is of the utmost importance on account of possible reflection from the surface of the paper or image structure. If the lamps are too far forward, i.e. too close to the lens axis, light will be reflected from the black lines or glass of the copy holder, resulting in fogged lines on the negative probably rendering it useless. If the lamps are too much to the side the illumination of the copy is seriously reduced and the effect of the grain of the copy surface or raised ink design

BOOK PATTERN COPY HOLDER

is accentuated. If the eye could be placed in the position of the lens, and the lamps then adjusted until all signs of reflection disappeared from the copy, it would probably be found that the lamps are at an angle of 45° from the centre of the copy. In fact, this angle can be taken as satisfactory and should be maintained for all standard work. A useful guide for lamp distance and angle can be made with three strips of wood joined in the form of a 45° triangle. Lamp distances are marked on the hypotenuse. The triangle is placed on the board with the point on the centre of the copy and the longest side extending outwards. The correct lamp distance and angle can thus be obtained without any possibility of error. The rays of the arc lamp must not be allowed to fall direct on the lens.

When focusing the image it is a common practice to open the

lens to full aperture, and the beginner is likely to get into this habit very readily on account of the brilliance of the image and

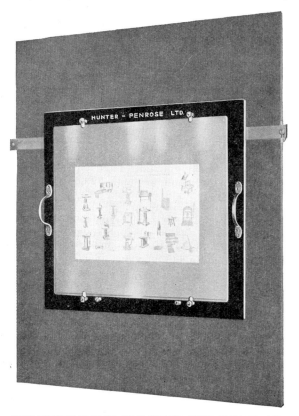

NEW PATTERN FACE-UP COPY HOLDER WITH CUSHION BACK

consequent ease of judgment of definition. This is faulty practice, however, and with critical work often leads to results which are not the best possible, particularly when the copy has to be considerably reduced in size. After a very short experience the operator can estimate the approximate size of stop which will be indicated by the scale for any enlargement or reduction, and the stop used for focusing should only be slightly larger than that used for the actual exposure; consistent, of course, with sufficient brilliance of image to enable accurate focusing.

Assuming that the first copy is to be reproduced same size, the lens is opened to, say, F/22 and adjustments made until the image becomes clear and well defined on the focusing screen. A special magnifying glass is used to examine finally the lines of the image. The image must be viewed on the matt surface of the screen, not through the clear diagonals which are usually provided as an aid to centralizing. Experienced operators, however, use the clear-glass portion in conjunction with the edge of the matt surface: that is, they carefully focus the magnifying glass on the matt surface and at the same time examine the "air image" through the clear portion. When critically focusing for definition, the image should be examined at a point about two-thirds of the distance from the centre to the outer edge.

Adjustments of the camera to obtain exact size together with perfect sharpness will be found rather difficult at first and as much practice as possible should be given to this operation, but it should not be continuous for any length of time owing to the strain on the eyes with unaccustomed conditions.

A celluloid rule is a useful accessory for measuring the required image size, but it must be remembered that celluloid can rarely be relied upon for absolute accuracy, and must be checked with a steel rule for critical measurements. The difficulty of measuring an image when it is separated from the rule by the thickness of the ground glass can be overcome by keeping the reflection of the eye in line with the point being measured. For final checking, the magnifier should be placed squarely over the rule and centred over the required ruling. If the eye is in line with the axis of the magnifier it is possible to check sizes with sufficient accuracy for all practical purposes.[1]

After completion of the focusing the image must be centred on the screen by operating the rise and fall movement of the lens board and moving the copy-board to left or right. The diagonal lines on the screen give an indication of the correct position, but a further facility is afforded by ruling pencil lines on the matt surface representing the positions occupied by standard sizes of negative glass, making allowance for the strips of film at the top and bottom of plates which are covered by the plate sticks in the dark-slide.

Reference should now be made to the spring tape at the side of the camera. The number of inches indicated by the pointer represents the number of 1/64 in. required for the diameter of the lens diaphragm, and when this is adjusted accordingly it will, of course, be 1/64 of the camera extension. This proportion has been found by practical experience to be the most generally useful for normal operations. If the image is projected to exactly the same size as the copy it will be found that the lens diaphragm is approximately F/32. The reason for any discrepancy is the difference between practical considerations and optical exactness. When one of these proportionate stop systems is employed the

[1] When absolute accuracy is required irrespective of time and trouble, for such work as map printing, replacing a broken negative of a colour set, etc., a useful method is to moisten (not gum) two small pieces of thin tin-foil and place them on the matt surface of the focusing screen, one exactly above the other and at the required distance apart, which can be accurately measured by means of a registering gauge or a steel rule and magnifying glass. The facing or measuring edges of the tin-foil should be about $\frac{1}{8}$ in. wide. When finally checking the projected image for size the lower edge or register mark can be brought into line with the corresponding edge of the tin-foil by carefully operating the rising front of the camera. If the upper edge of the image is only the merest fraction out of alignment with the upper tin-foil a slight adjustment of the front body only will not noticeably affect the sharpness of the image, particularly if a smaller stop than usual is used for the exposure.

operator can for all immediate purposes ignore the "F" numbers of the lens.

The camera is always provided with locking devices to prevent accidental movement of any part which would affect the focus of the image. While later these will perhaps only be used when making colour sets, it is advisable that at the commencement the camera is locked immediately after focusing every job.

SECTION 2. MAKING THE NEGATIVE (WET COLLODION)

To prepare glass for wet collodion it must be thoroughly cleaned, and for this purpose new glass is placed in the soaking trough (Solution No. 1) for several hours and then well scrubbed with the glass-cleaning brush. Glass which has been previously used for negatives should be soaked for at least 24 hours. If varnish has been used on the negatives it must first be cleaned off by soaking in a 20 per cent solution of commercial caustic soda to which has been added a small proportion of methylated spirit.

For the final scrubbing a glass-cleaning vice is useful for holding the glass firmly. Water should be allowed to run over the surface while scrubbing. Special attention must be given to the edges, particularly when the glass has been used previously, for particles of old collodion film are easily overlooked and if allowed to remain would help to pollute the silver bath.

The collodion with which the plate is coated will not by itself adhere firmly to the glass during the several manipulations. To overcome this difficulty a coating of albumen solution, or an albumen substratum as it is called (Solution No. 2) may be used. After making sure that the glass is absolutely clean, the well-filtered albumen substratum is flowed over, preferably twice to ensure an even and completely coated surface. Care should be taken that the solution does not creep to the under side of the glass as it would eventually be dissolved and deposited in the silver bath. For the same reason one must disregard the frequent recommendation to dip the glass in a dish of albumen solution. This method was advised to avoid any doubt as to which was the coated surface when the plate was dry. The coated glass is placed in the drying cabinet, care being taken to place the coated side of all plates facing the same way.

A number of plates in excess of anticipated requirements should always be in readiness as a considerable amount of valuable time is wasted if, following a "slip," glass has to be cleaned and coated and allowed to dry before another negative can be made.

An alternative method of securing the collodion film to the glass is by edging the glass with a thin deposit of rubber solution. When the collodion is flowed over the plate it will adhere to the edging and withstand any subsequent treatment in the sink.

The porcelain dish or dishes used for the silver bath should be kept for this purpose only. Sufficient thoroughly filtered solution (Solution No. 3) is placed in the dish to give a depth of at least $\frac{3}{4}$ in. It is most decidedly a false economy to attempt to employ too small a quantity of solution as this only leads to "silver bath marks" and other troubles which precede spoilt negatives. A shallow varnished wood cover over the silver bath helps to keep the solution clean.

Before using a freshly prepared bath a collodion-coated plate should be allowed to stand in the solution for a couple of hours. Alternatively, it has been recommended to add 4 or 5 gr of potassium iodide to each pint of solution. A bath which has been in use continuously collects a certain amount of alcohol from the collodion and consequently it is better to leave the solution in the dish during the night instead of pouring it back into the bottle. The large surface thus exposed to the air permits most of the alcohol to evaporate. The bath cover which normally rests on the top of the dish should be propped up to allow free access of air. The sheet of albumen-coated glass which is to be used for the negative should be of sufficient size to allow at least an inch margin all round the image. Glass for immediate use should be polished by a rag dipped in industrial spirit and iodine.

A special collodion pouring bottle is preferably employed, but if an ordinary bottle is used all traces of dried collodion which rapidly collect on the neck of the bottle must be removed. The safe-light for wet collodion is orange or deep yellow, but a white light is permissible and advised while actually coating the plate with collodion. During this operation the plate is preferably held by means of a Pneumatic Plate-holding Bulb, otherwise heat from the hand is likely to cause uneven patches. Hold the plate horizontally by the left hand and carefully pour a pool of collodion to cover about one-third of the total area in the far right quarter, slightly tilt the plate until the collodion runs first to the far left corner, then the near left, and finally to the near right corner from which it is drained through a funnel into the excess bottle. When the whole plate is thus coated it is tilted to an angle of about 65° or 70° to complete the draining. It is extremely important that while in this draining position the plate is rocked slowly to the left and right in order to avoid the streaky marks which would occur if the collodion were allowed to drain in one direction only.

The amount of collodion required, the avoidance of running over the edge and on to the back of the plate, the formation of a coating of even thickness and equal setting, are all points of judgment upon which the operator will have to rely on practice and experience.

When coating large plates there is a very real difficulty in obtaining an even coating, and it will be found preferable to use a thinner collodion with a slight excess of alcohol and keep the plate in the nearly horizontal position for a longer period.

The thinner collodion is of course more difficult to manipulate, but it is assumed that by the time large plates have to be prepared the operator has acquired the necessary skill in this direction.

Immediately the collodion becomes tacky the plate is placed in the silver bath. To do this, raise the left end of the dish, rest one end of the plate on the drained end of the dish, lower the other end of the plate until it is nearly touching the solution, and finally release the plate, at the same time lowering the dish to the horizontal position. Care should be taken not to put the fingers into the solution ($AgNO_3$). The operation needs great care, owing to the necessity of obtaining a perfectly even and full flow of solution over the entire surface.

Any hesitation or too vigorous handling will probably result in "bath marks" which will be noticeable in the developed negative in various forms, such as a line of weak film with a strip of graded density on one side, or numerous small splash marks of weaker density. Once the plate has been placed in the bath it must be kept totally immersed for at least two minutes. If the solution is allowed to drain off part of the surface immediately after immersion, bath marks are almost sure to be the result. This, however, should not occur if a bath of adequate quantity is used. The dish should be rocked in both directions occasionally during immersion of the plate. The time required until the film is ready for use will vary slightly according to temperature and condition of the bath, but three minutes is an average period when working at a temperature of 65° F.

If the plate is raised at one end before it is ready it may be seen that the surface presents a greasy appearance and the solution will drain off in irregular streaks. (A special silver-bath hook is used to raise the plate; this is made of either silver wire or highly glazed ebonite.) When the plate is entirely free from these conditions and presents an even smooth surface upon being raised, it is completely sensitized, that is, part of the silver in the solution has reacted with the iodides and bromides, etc., suspended in the collodion film, forming silver haloids, principally silver iodide which in conjunction with silver nitrate is sensitive to light. This necessary presence of silver nitrate accounts for the use of the plate while it is still wet with a small amount of silver solution on the film surface. A plate which has started to dry becomes practically useless, and precautions against this have to be taken when working in hot dry weather and giving lengthy exposures. A piece of wet blotting paper on the back of the glass helps to a certain extent, and in extreme cases recourse has been made to the addition of pure glycerine to both the silver bath and collodion up to about 5 per cent.

The sensitized plate is held for a short period over the bath to drain and then placed on the bench and leaning against the wall. Both of these surfaces should be provided with clean pads of blotting paper. The back and edges of the glass are then cleaned with blotting paper, and a small strip should also be placed on the lower plate stick of the dark-slide. This will absorb any solution which drains off the plate while it is in position. Should such solution be allowed to remain in the dark-slide it would dry and the re-crystallized silver would be picked up by capillary attraction and deposited on the surface of following plates, causing ruinous markings. The plate sticks should always be wiped free from solution immediately after use, and together with the leading edge of the roller blind and the receiving slot should periodically be thoroughly cleaned and given a coating of shellac varnish as a precautionary measure against the corrosive action of silver nitrate.

Before placing the plate in the dark-slide, check the position of the lower plate stick, which must be at the correct height according to the size of plate or position of the image. When the plate is gripped between the two plate sticks the dark-slide door is positioned and this usually has a leaf spring which holds the plate firmly against the plate stops. (These stops, by the way, should be of silver to minimize injurious chemical action.)

The dark-slide is placed on the back of the camera, where it is held securely by special quick-action clamps or spring catches. After making sure that the lens cap is on the lens, the roller blind is gently drawn down and the arc lamps switched on. When the camera has steadied itself the lens cap is removed, and replaced after the required interval: a trial exposure may be from 20 to 60 seconds according to the intensity of the illumination. When closing the dark-slide shutter the left hand should be placed on the top of the dark-slide, or lifting handle, to prevent it lifting before the shutter is closed. A small bolt is often fixed to the side of the back body for the same purpose.

To return to the dark-room, the plate is removed from the slide and held in a horizontal position over the sink. A small quantity of Iron Developer (Solution No. 4) is placed in a beaker (say 2 oz for a 10 in. × 8 in. plate) and the flowed quickly and smoothly over the plate surface. The flow of the developer should start at the left-hand corner and pass rapidly to the right, the plate being slightly tilted as necessary to maintain an even and quick spread of solution over the whole surface. If the operation is carried out in a too vigorous or uncontrolled manner the developer will wash away the small quantity of silver nitrate remaining on the film. This must be avoided as the presence of silver nitrate is an essential factor during development. The developer mixing with the silver solution reduces the silver and deposits it on the light-acted portion of the film.

The plate is rocked slightly during development and as much of the solution as possible retained on the surface. The image should appear almost immediately and should be complete in about 20 seconds at 65° F. Forced development following an under-exposure will only result in a grainy effect being produced in the clear portions of the film: over-exposure results in the immediate flashing up of the image and general fogging or veiling. The appearance of a correctly exposed and developed plate is difficult to describe beyond saying that the image appears as a warm dark grey deposit on the cream coloured background. The plate is placed under a good flow of water immediately development appears complete, and allowed to wash for a minute or longer. The amount of acid restrainer in the developer will probably have to be increased during hot weather to keep the reaction under proper control. Ferrous ammonium sulphate is sometimes found preferable to ferrous sulphate under conditions where the developer oxidizes rapidly, and the proportion of the former should be increased by 50 per cent. Alcohol should not be required at all with a new or perfectly conditioned bath and is only added to assist the even flowing of the developer over the plate. A film which has been sensitized in an old bath from which the alcohol has not evaporated tends to repel the developer and only sufficient alcohol need be added to overcome this effect.

The developed and washed plate is flowed over with Cyanide Fixing solution (Solution No. 5) which dissolves the silver haloids, leaving a finely divided silver image on the surface of the film. By using a dipper for the cyanide, one avoids the fumes of prussic acid.

The application of fixing solution must be continued until all trace of creamy appearance disappears. If only a strip of unfixed film remains where the collodion has thickened during the draining off, this strip may be removed with a small piece of wood during the subsequent washing. Any such unfixed portion of film if allowed to remain would cause stains which would probably spread to the image.

The plate can now be worked in white light and is flowed

over with Copper Bromide Intensifier (Solution No. 8). This solution bleaches the image, which is then carefully washed. The washing at this stage must be limited and a continuous flow of water on one place avoided as the structure of the image is partly soluble.

The plate is drained to get rid of excess water and then flooded with Blackening Silver (Solution No. 9) which again turns the image black. Copper and silver intensifying solutions may be used in glass or porcelain dishes when the size of work permits and so prevent the waste which is difficult to avoid when pouring solutions on and off a plate. Vertical dipping baths are very convenient for this purpose and occupy but little space at the side of the sink.

Further washing is followed by bleaching with Iodine Intensifier (Solution No. 10) and the plate again washed. The image can now be seen very clearly and must be examined critically with a magnifying glass. If any veil or fog appears on the clear portions it can be cleared by evenly flowing over a very weak solution of cyanide made by *thoroughly* mixing a few drops of fixing solution with 10 oz of water. After each application the film must be rinsed and examined to note the effect. If any doubt exists as to the extent to which reduction should be taken, it is far better to under-estimate than over-estimate the required treatment. The former may be rectified sub-sequently by giving a slightly longer exposure when printing on metal, but the latter would render the negative useless by opening up the lines too much and reducing the density of the film.

After thorough washing, the film is finally blackened with Sulphide Blackening solution (Solution No. 11), and washed immediately the film has blackened right through. This operation should be carried through at the outside sink owing to the extreme ill-effects of the fumes if freed in the dark-room. A

short application of a very weak (say 1 per cent) solution of
nitric acid is advisable as a precaution against stains. The
sulphide solution must not be drained back into the pouring
bottle.

The collodion film is very fragile and care must be taken at
all times during the foregoing operations that nothing but
liquid is allowed to come in contact with it. The finished
negative needs some protection against rubbing and scratching,
and for ordinary purposes it is sufficient to flow over a
10 per cent gum solution, after the final washing and before
drying.

If the negative is wanted immediately it may be dried by heat,
but the glass must not be made so hot that a draught of cold air
might crack it.

When a negative is likely to be subjected to repeated handling
it must be varnished, and for this purpose special negative
varnishes are available, or a varnish can be made with best
orange shellac 3 oz (75 g), methylated spirit or alcohol 40 oz
(1000 c.c.). After dissolving, this should be allowed to stand
for a day or two, then decanted and one dram (3 c.c.) of castor
oil added. The plate must be dried and heated before applying
the varnish, which is flowed over the plate in a similar manner
to the collodion, except that it will probably be found easier
to allow the varnish to flow from one end of the plate to the
other instead of from corner to corner. While draining, the
plate should be dried by radiated heat (not over a gas ring,
which might set the varnish on fire).

An alternative to a spirit varnish can be made as follows:
Boil one gallon (4000 c.c.) of water and completely dissolve
about one pound (400 g) of borax. While still boiling add
20 oz (500 g) crushed white shellac and stir for several minutes.
Allow the solution to stand for several hours and then decant,
preferably by a syphon arrangement. This water varnish can

be flowed over the negative after the final washing. When the negative is finished with, it will be found that the glass can be cleaned much more readily than one which has been coated with spirit varnish.

Lead intensification is frequently used in place of the previously described copper and silver process. It is both quicker and cheaper, but has not the same latitude of manipulation. With skilled hands, however, excellent results are obtained even with poor copies which require negative manipulation.

The negative is carried through in the normal manner as far as fixing and washing, but any reduction or clearing must be effected at this stage, and requires experienced judgment particularly when dealing with difficult subjects where perhaps the paper is slightly discoloured or the lines of the design are of unequal density. The reducer consists of a weak solution of cyanide (Solution No. 5 diluted) to which has been added sufficient Potassium Ferricyanide solution (Solution No. 6) to turn it lemon yellow. This is flowed over the film and the plate rocked for a few seconds, then washed. The effect of each application of the reducer is better observed by examining the surface of the plate under a good light rather than looking through the back of the glass. When the lines are deemed to be quite clear with no deposit which would subsequently intensify, the film is bleached with Lead Nitrate solution (Solution No. 7) and then washed, preferably with warm water, until the light yellow appearance of the film turns almost white. The bleached film should be kept away from strong white light as much as possible. A short application of a 1 per cent solution of hydrochloric acid or nitric acid is advisable during the washing. The final blackening, etc., is as described previously.

While it has just been stated that it is necessary to reduce before intensifying, and this is certainly the general procedure, there is a comparatively little-used method of reduction which is possible

after the final blackening. The bleached negative is washed for
rather less time than usual and the acid wash omitted. Blacken
the film and rinse, then bleach as far as necessary the edges of
the lines or the veil it is desired to remove with—

Potassium permanganate	.	30 grains			2 g
Sulphuric acid .	.	. ¼ oz	or		7 c.c.
Water	. .	. 10 oz			280 c.c.

Wash, and dissolve the bleached film with—

Ammonium acetate .	.	3 oz	or	100 g
Water	. .	. 9 oz		300 c.c.

Should a slight brown stain still remain after washing, this can be
removed by soaking in a saturated solution of oxalic acid. If
necessary the film can be blackened again with a 10 per cent
solution of sodium sulphide.

Another rather unusual procedure might be described here
but it is only a suggestion to deal with an emergency. It sometimes occurs that a negative after the final blackening is found
to be lacking in density, perhaps in one portion only. Misjudgment or faulty treatment has occurred at some stage, and
while it would be better to make a new negative it may be
possible to obtain a printable result by further intensification.
To one part of iodine solution (No. 10) add two parts of copper
solution (No. 8) and immediately apply the mixture to the weak
portion of the film until it is bleached. Wash gently for about
30 sec and re-blacken with a clean solution of sodium sulphide.

To return to normal procedure, the completed and varnished
negative is sent to the artists' department where any pin-holes
are "spotted." Care must be taken that the opaquing medium is
applied as thinly as possible; any raised or lumpy deposits will
cause lack of contact between the film and the metal plate when
printing down.

There should be an opaque margin around the image either

to the edge of the glass, or to a depth of at least $1\frac{1}{2}$ in. around the design when using glass considerably larger than the image. Instead of painting out this margin it is preferable to use thin tinfoil. This is supplied in rolls, and care must be taken when unrolling that the sheets of foil are not damaged. The unrolled sheets should be kept in a flat box such as a dry-plate box. Strips of varying width are cut by placing, say, half a dozen sheets on clean glass and using a steel straight-edge and a sharp knife. The cut must be absolutely "clean," otherwise difficulty will be experienced in separating the strips without tearing. To attach a strip to the negative, place the foil on clean paper and lightly smear with gum or paste in two or three places, using the side of the hand to ensure that only an extremely thin film remains, otherwise it is improbable that it would dry before printing down and then the applied pressure would force the liquid gum from under the foil and possibly ruin the print. A weak rubber solution may be used in place of the gum. This tin-foil is extremely thin, and lack of contact will not occur through its use even where overlapping occurs at corners. Obtaining opacity by painting out with the usual mediums frequently results in a comparatively thick coating.

SECTION 3. CARE OF THE SILVER BATH

This solution is the most important of those used in the process, and too much stress cannot be laid upon the necessity of absolute cleanliness of everthing with which it is brought into contact. While various methods of more or less elaboration have been recommended for "restoring" or purifying an old bath, it has been found by practical experience that, providing proper care has been taken throughout, a bath can be used almost indefinitely by the simplest treatment.

It must be realized that each ounce of collodion takes approximately 15 gr of silver nitrate from the bath by chemical change and surface adhesion. (This loss must be made good by the addition of silver nitrate and distilled water as necessary.) At the same time other nitrates are formed in the bath, and after a period of use it becomes over-iodized and pin-holes are caused in the film. The bath should then be diluted with about a third or half its bulk of water, neutralized with a few grains of sodium carbonate and allowed to stand in all available sunlight or strong daylight for two or three days. The excess iodides will be precipitated and the solution can then be filtered and made up to strength and acidified.

If the above treatment results in an unwanted quantity the bath may be boiled down to the required bulk in an evaporating basin before filtering. This operation also disposes of any alcohol which has not evaporated while the bath has been standing idle.

There is still a general practice of continued boiling down of a silver bath until a paste and then a liquid is formed to which is added distilled water. In the author's experience this has always been of doubtful value, and assuming that correct treatment is given throughout in disposing of alcohol (by evaporating from a shallow dish), exposure to daylight, making up to strength and careful filtering, a bath can be employed almost indefinitely; in cases of excessive contamination the bath may be treated with a strong filtered solution of potassium permanganate. When added gradually this turns the silver solution pink, but it rapidly turns to a muddy brown colour and then slightly clears again. The treatment should be continued until the pink colour is retained for about 15 minutes. The solution is placed in daylight for two or three days and carefully filtered.

SECTION 4. GENERAL FAULTS

The described operations in the production of a wet collodion negative appear reasonably straightforward and free from trouble. If due precautions are taken, and extreme climatic conditions do not have to be contended with, the process should in fact be of the desired simplicity. However, troubles certainly do arise through adverse temporary conditions, negligence, misjudgment or impure chemicals, etc.

We will attempt to explain as many such faults as have come to our knowledge and are likely to occur with average conditions. Certain additional faults with obscure causes occasionally arise, however, but after careful examination of all factors the trouble is invariably traced to either direct or indirect effects of injurious fumes, dirt or impurities at some period.

The Film Becomes Loose while in the Silver Bath

Incomplete or too thin coating of albumen substratum; dirty glass; too much acid in the silver bath or too prolonged immersion; use of old collodion.

Wavy or "Crapy" Marks on the Sensitized Film

Insufficient setting of the collodion before immersion.

Curved Line of Lighter Coloured Film, Probably Graded on One Side

Uneven flowing of the bath over the film surface upon immersing.

Splash Marks on the Film

As above, or interrupted immersion of part of the surface during the early stages of sensitizing.

Gritty Surface of the Film when taken from the Bath

Possibly too much iodide in the bath; bath requires reconditioning.

Uneven Spreading of the Developer over the Plate Surface

Use of an old bath and a developer short of or lacking alcohol. (The developer formula given in the list of solutions included spirit as a standard component, but it is not essential with a new bath.)

Black Uneven Marks or "Fog" Appearing after Application of the Developer, and Spreading and Increasing in Density over the Whole Surface

Badly ventilated dark-room; impure acetic acid in the developer. If the former, the effect will probably not occur when starting work in the morning, but the trouble will gradually increase. A rough test for acetic acid is to add a few drops of pure silver nitrate solution to $\frac{1}{4}$ oz of the acid in a perfectly clean measure or test tube. Resulting cloudiness or turbidity indicates impurities reacting with the silver. (Chemicals should always be obtained from a reputable supply house specializing in photographic materials in order to avoid the above and numerous other troubles which frequently occur following the use of locally purchased chemicals.)

"Veiling" or Slight Fog over the Whole or Part of the Film

Action of light in the camera or dark-room. The portions of film protected by the plate-stops in the dark-slide afford a rough indication of the cause of the trouble. If these portions remain perfectly clear, examine the camera for light leakage through holes or cracks in the bellows, a badly fitting rising front board, strong reflections from some outside source, internal reflections, etc. If the fog occurs on the portion of the film protected while in the dark-slide, the fault lies in the use of an unsuitable safe-light; allowing direct rays to fall on the film while in the silver bath or at any time while in the sensitive condition; allowing the film to be exposed for too long a period to light which for all practical purposes is quite "safe"; or light leakage through the sides of doors or windows. A similar fogging of the plate might be caused by too warm or insufficiently restrained developer; an insufficiently acidified bath; or use of an un-suitable albumen or a decomposed substratum solution.

Fine Lines Fogged

Reflection from copy due to wrong position of arc lamps. Over-exposure, particularly if original is an impression from an engraved plate.

Film of Scum Formed During Development

This is a light grey deposit which can be washed away under a flow of water by lightly rubbing with a wad of cotton wool. If the scum is heavy the image will appear weak and under-exposed and it is better to locate and rectify the cause and start afresh. Any of the following might be the source of the trouble: dark-room at a higher temperature than the camera room; fumes of paint, turpentine, gas, ammonia, sulphides, etc.; smoke or fumes from burning arcs; insufficient acid in the silver bath, or too long a period between sensitizing and developing, in which case it might be advantageous to re-immerse the plate in a separate silver bath before developing. In cases of doubt a cure can often be effected by the addition of a few drops of a filtered solution of potassium permanganate.

Heavy Tree-like Growth of Scum Starting from the Edge of the Plate

Aptly termed "oysters," these are caused by dirt or dried silver solution on the dark-slide sticks, which upon contact with the wet surface of the film has spread inwards by capillary attraction.

Dirty Marks and Streaks

Insufficiently cleaned glass; use of a dirty dusting brush.

Grain in Clear Portions of the Film

Prolonged development as an attempt to correct under-exposure.

Uneven Density

Uneven illumination; partial drying of the film before immersion in the bath or during exposure; uneven coating of collodion; uneven distribution of the developer; local application of reducing or intensifying solutions; or too much washing after copper intensification.

Irregular Blackening of the Image on Applying the Blackening Silver

Too much surface water on the film; impurities or insufficient acid in the blackening solution; or solution too weak.

White Markings on Application of the Blackening Silver

Insufficient washing after copper intensification. It will be noted that too much or too little washing at this stage is liable to cause trouble. As there is no visual indication of the correct amount, the operator will have to judge by experience.

Weak Image when Exposure and other Factors are Known to be Correct

Old collodion; over-acidified bath; or bath too weak.

Small Transparent Spots or "Pin-holes" and "Coinets" of Different Sizes Scattered Irregularly over the Film

Floor and chemical dust (particularly hypo) in the camera body or dark-room; insufficiently filtered silver bath or substratum.

Regular Distributions of Small Pin-holes over the Whole Surface

An over-iodized silver bath.

Black Spots and Marks

Insufficiently filtered substratum; chemical dust falling on the plate before or during coating with collodion; dust or specks of dried collodion in the pouring bottle.

Fine Black Lines

Scratches on the glass surface; glass imperfectly cleaned.

Film Cracking

Over-intensification, particularly with lead. Contributing factors: albumen coating too thin; collodion too thick; prolonged drying before immersion, or uneven drying by heat. Excess ether in the collodion, while perhaps giving a harder film, might render it subject to cracking.

Denser Portions of the Film Adjacent to Large Areas of Clear Film

The fault is more likely to occur with a new silver bath in conjunction with a weak and insufficiently restrained developer or when there is only a small amount of silver solution left on the surface of the film prior to development or during development. The developer acts on the free silver solution, depositing metallic silver on the light-acted parts. If the developer is not well restrained this action will occur more quickly following the flow of the developer over those portions where there has been no light action and consequently no deposition.

Brown Deposit when Finally Blackened

Over-exposure and under-development with consequent low deposit of metallic silver; sulphide too strong or too old.

Stains

Insufficient washing at some stage. Insufficient fixation. Stains can sometimes be removed after final blackening with a weak cyanide solution.

The Completed Image Appears Loose and "Flaky"

Use of too strong intensifying solutions, particularly iodine and sulphide.

Opalescent Appearance of the Film after Varnishing

Plate too cold. (If the plate is too hot or not rocked during draining a streaky effect might result.)

Double or Blurred Image

Heavy vibration of camera during exposure: insecure mounting of the lens or prism. If there is the slightest movement of any component part, the least vibration of the camera will cause a blurred image. Such vibration would normally be ineffectual, for it would be common to both camera and copy-board when using spring suspension camera stands.

Horizontal and Vertical Lines not in the same Focus (Astigmatism)

Unsuitable lens or lens prism combination.

Generally Poor Definition when the Lens and Camera are Known to be Satisfactory

Focusing with the lens aperture fully open and then stopping down to a very small aperture, particularly when reducing from a large copy. The act of stopping down has two effects; the more important is the increase of the depth of focus and quality of definition. The other effect which occurs to a varying degree with different lenses is a slight movement of the focal plane. While this latter effect is mostly covered by the former, it is obvious that when using the lens at anywhere near its full covering capacity the best possible results can be obtained only by focusing with a lens aperture as near to the exposing aperture as is consistent with adequate viewing brilliance. Modern lenses, however, are reasonably free from "stop difference."

SECTION 5. USE OF THE PRISM

A reversal process is required for the production of: negatives which are to be followed by contact positives for one of the offset reversal processes; plates for a direct printing press; offset plates from a reversed original. Such originals have frequently to be dealt with where original litho stones or plates have been in use for making up offset plates by the transfer process. Impressions from these "originals" will of course be reversed.

The camera is rotated on the turn-table until it bears against the stops provided. The prism is screwed securely on the front mount of the lens and then by unlocking the slip ring it can be further rotated until the face of the prism is exactly parallel with the copy-board. If the camera and copy-board have been trued up with a spirit-level this can also be used for ascertaining the correct position of the prism. Some manufacturers, particularly when dealing with the larger sizes, arrange for the prism to be placed next to the lens board with the lens facing the copy-board.

When the use of a spirit-level is not practicable the following method of lining-up should be used.

Draw an accurate fine line square on Bristol board and attach securely to the copy-board. Focus to same size, using a card strip with two knife cuts for measuring. Place a focusing eye-piece directly over the cut when measuring to avoid parallax. Adjust the turn-table stops until the two vertical lines are exactly equal. Adjust the prism until the two horizontal lines are exactly equal. When entirely satisfied that the square is an exact undistorted reproduction, place a straight-edge on the prism, and mark the sides of the lens board in line with the upper edge. When positioning the prism in future it may be turned until accurate sighting brings the straight-edge into correct alignment.

The copy-board is moved over to the left on the runners or slides provided and the lamps repositioned accordingly. Focusing will perhaps seem a little more difficult at first as the whole carriage has to be adjusted. The exposures will have to be increased slightly, and the nominal covering capacity of the lens may be reduced; consequently when making full-size critical negatives it may be necessary to stop down the lens to a smaller aperture than was used when working direct.

If a prism has not been included in the equipment and some sudden requirement renders the production of a reversed negative essential, it is possible to make this either by "stripping," which is described on page 92, or by placing the plate in the dark-slide with the back of the glass which has been thoroughly cleaned facing the lens. The spring on the dark-slide door must be removed to prevent damaging the film. If due care is exercised the grip of the plate sticks is sufficient to hold the plate against the stops. (If it is deemed essential to use the spring, the film of an unbacked dry plate may be protected by smooth paper and a piece of card cut to size: in the case of wet collodion a second piece of glass may be used with a narrow strip of card at each side to keep the two surfaces from touching.) When employing this method the back body must be moved forward after focusing, to an extent equal to the thickness of the glass, in order to bring the sensitive film into the correct focal plane.

CHAPTER IV

STUDIO WORK—DRY PLATES AND FILMS

SECTION 1. DRY PLATES

ALTHOUGH many departments specializing in finest quality line work retain wet collodion exclusively, the use of gelatine emulsion on glass, film and paper is extending very rapidly, and the manufacturers are catering for every possible requirement.

The modern Process Dry Plate gives clean contrasty results when worked correctly that compare very favourably in printing quality with the wet collodion plate. The primary difference between the images of the two plates is that in the former the dense image is incorporated *in* the gelatine film, while it is built on the *surface* of the collodion film. However, in spite of the one-time prejudice, extremely good results can definitely be obtained with dry plates even when reproducing critical line work.

Many firms who employ both processes on the same camera have separate dark-slides in the interest of cleanliness, and this is by no means an extravagance.

The dry-plate dark-room should have plate cupboards and a bench well removed from the sink. A bench at each side of the sink accommodates the dishes for developing and fixing. Racks for these should be built beneath the benches. The dark-room illumination is the same as for wet collodion—orange or deep yellow—and the same precautions must be taken against direct rays from the lamp falling on the undeveloped plate.

The plates are preferably "backed" to prevent halation effects, and it is essential to state this requirement when ordering.

The manipulation of dry plates is extremely simple, and for

certain classes of work the extra cost is well balanced by the saving of the operator's time.

After focusing as previously described, a plate is positioned centrally in the dark-slide and an exposure made which will only be a fraction of that given for wet collodion. The exact exposure working with the standardized stops and illumination will have to be ascertained by trial, but will probably be 4 or 5 sec with conditions previously described. This is with the general-purpose type of process plate which has a nominal rated speed of H and D 25. With such short exposures and for black and white work the speed is not of paramount importance, and manufacturers are now realizing that the more important properties are maximum contrast, cleanliness and fine grain. A thin emulsion consistent with adequate density is an advantage in connexion with quick development, washing, and drying.

Several types of line plates and films are now listed by each manufacturer; emulsions rated about H and D 10 will be found entirely satisfactory for camera line negatives.

A formula for the most suitable developer for the make of plate is always printed on the box or enclosed leaflet, but it will be found that the majority approximate to the following—

No. 1

			or	
Hydroquinone	.	1 oz		25 g
Potassium metabisulphite	.	1 oz		25 g
Potassium bromide	.	1 oz		25 g
Water up to	. .	40 oz		1000 c.c.

No. 2

			or	
Pot. hydrate	. .	2 oz		50 g
Water up to	. .	40 oz		1000 c.c.

It is necessary to keep these solutions in separate bottles and mix equal quantities of each immediately before use. The bottles

must be well shaken before taking any solution. Until the operator has acquired a thorough knowledge of dry-plate working
he is advised to use the developer for one negative only. Development of the trial plate should be continued with gentle rocking
in both directions for at least 2½ to 3 min at 65°F, and then the
plate rinsed and fixed in the hypo bath—

Potassium metabisulphite	.	2 oz	or	50 g
Sodium hyposulphite (hypo)		16 oz		400 g
Water up to	.	. 40 oz		1000 c.c.

The use of an old fixing bath often results in the refusal of the
film to clear, even after prolonged immersion. When the trial
negative is examined an estimate of the correct exposure can
readily be made: the aim should be a negative which after full
development shows clear bright lines on a dense ground.
Cutting down development following an over-exposure, or
endeavouring to force development after an under-exposure,
gives results much inferior to those obtained with correct
exposure and development. Should a plate be slightly over-
exposed, the development should still be carried through to the
full extent as this will help to maintain the required extreme
contrast. The density of the background will, of course, be in
excess of normal and the clear portions veiled, but this latter
may be removed and the contrast maintained or improved by
subsequent reduction without impairing the density of the background. Reduction and intensification are not generally
necessary to obtain a good printing negative, particularly with
the improved modern dry plates with steep gradation, but can
sometimes be employed with advantage when photographing
a faulty or difficult original, or following misjudgment of
exposure or development.

The most common reducing solution is that known as
Farmer's Reducer. Sufficient 10 per cent solution of potassium

ferricyanide is added to a 10 per cent solution of hypo to turn this pale yellow. The operator will quickly learn to estimate the effective strength of the solution by its colour. The deeper the colour the more quickly will the solution act. (The foregoing applies to colour at time of mixing.) Too much ferricyanide, however, will probably cause stains. A special hypo solution should be kept prepared for this purpose, otherwise there is the temptation to use some of the fixing bath, and this might also lead to bad stains.

Extreme care must be exercised when reducing, to keep the action under full control. Until experience has been gained there is a very common tendency, particularly after working with wet collodion, to "over-cut" the negative owing to lack of attention to the fact that reduction is likely to continue until the active solution is completely washed out of the film. It is consequently much better to make several applications with a fairly weak solution than attempt to obtain the full reduction at one operation. It will be noticed that the solution rapidly loses its effect, and a few drops of the ferricyanide solution must repeatedly be added when using the reducer for any length of time.

When the lines are perfectly clear, or as clear as possible without "spreading," the negative is thoroughly washed for five or ten minutes, and then if intensification is required it is bleached by rocking in the following—

Dry Plate Intensifier

Mercury bichloride	.	. 100 gr		12 g
Potassium bromide	.	. 100 gr	or	12 g
Water up to	.	. 10 oz		500 c.c.

This bleaching solution may be used several times.

After a very thorough washing during which the film is

lightly rubbed with cotton-wool the negative is blackened by placing it in a 10 per cent solution of ammonia 0·880.

A short wash, and the negative is ready for drying; this can be accelerated if necessary by lightly dabbing both slides of the plate with a clean chamois leather and immersing in methylated spirit for a few minutes. The spirit bath may be kept for use with several negatives as a small quantity of water is not injurious, in fact it helps to prevent the slight cloudy effect which sometimes occurs following the use of pure spirit. This opalescent appearance will also arise if the plate has not been thoroughly washed at the required periods and is subsequently dried with spirit.

General Notes

Elimination of hypo from the film during washing can be speeded up and progress indicated by adding a few drops of *filtered* potassium permanganate solution to the washing dish. The resulting pink colour of the water quickly turns brown so long as hypo remains in the film. When after repeated operations the clean pink colour of the water remains unaltered the negative may be considered free from hypo.

Temperature is an important factor in all photographic work and solutions should be kept at approximately the same temperature, preferably that of the washing water, providing that this is not lower than 55°F. Any sudden change of temperature to which the film is subjected might cause frilling or reticulation. If it is desired to harden the gelatine film to prevent such reticulation the negative may be immersed for a few seconds in chrome alum 1 oz (25 g), water 4 oz (100 c.c.), immediately after development and before fixing.

A brown fog or stain is sometimes complained of after intensification: this is due to silver or mercury remaining in the film. The trouble arises through the use of a weak or exhausted fixing bath, insufficient fixing, exposure to light before the plate is thoroughly fixed, or insufficient washing before or after bleaching. It is a common and well-advised plan to leave the plate in the fixing solution for an additional period equal to that required to clear the film of its original opalescent appearance. The use of a second fresh fixing bath is sometimes resorted to when intensification is contemplated.

A persistent yellow stain is sometimes experienced on completion of development. If all normal precautions have been taken it may be assumed that the developer is not suitable for the make of plate, and an improvement will be effected by reducing the amount of bromide.

Owing to the present extensive requirements of contact negatives and positives for various purposes, the plate and film manufacturers have produced special emulsions which are of fine grain and produce maximum contrast. The slow speed of this class of plate is rather an advantage than otherwise. Emulsions having the characteristics of the Ilford Thin Film Half-tone or Line Film, which are excellent examples of this type, are developed with the usual hydroquinone-caustic developer. Catalogues and instructional leaflets issued by the several manufacturers should be obtained periodically, to keep the student informed as to the latest recommendations for all classes of work.

SECTION 2. CONTINUOUS-TONE NEGATIVES

These are often required for bromide prints, etc., and although specially suitable plates are available for all conditions, the more rapid type of process plate or film is quite satisfactory for the purpose in conjunction with full exposure and a "soft" developer such as—

Amidol	.	.	.	.	25–30 gr		5–6 g
Sodium sulphite		.	.	250 gr	or	50 g
Water	.	.	.	10 oz		875 c.c.

or—

A.	Sodium sulphite	.	.	5 oz	} or {	100 g	
	Pyro	.	.	¾ oz		15 g	
	Water up to	.	.	30 oz		600 c.c.	
B.	Sodium carbonate	.	.	1¾ oz	} or {	35 g	
	Pot. bromide	.	.	150 gr		7 g	
	Water up to	.	.	30 oz		600 c.c.	
C.	Sod. hydrate	.	.	1 oz	} or {	20 g	
	Water	.	.	8 oz		160 c.c.	

Take 25 parts A, 25 parts B, 1 part C, and use immediately after mixing. Development should be complete in three minutes at 70°F. Particular care must be taken regarding the temperature of the developer for this class of work, for a slight variation with the same developing time will give a very different result to previous negatives made under standard conditions. The necessity for this precaution is emphasized when dealing with an unusually large negative together, perhaps, with a tricky copy, and the operator deems it advisable to make a trial exposure on a small plate. The trial plate is almost useless as a guide unless the developer is exactly the same as that to be used for the large plate. It should preferably be taken from the same mixed solution and the two quantities should be tested with the thermometer and kept at an equal temperature. The proportion of developer to area of plate should also be approximately the same.

The necessity for reduction or intensification of continuous-tone negatives should be obviated as much as possible, but the judicious use of the previously mentioned reducer and intensifier might occasionally be of assistance when it is desired to increase the contrast of a developed negative.

A reducer which tends to act on the high-lights more quickly than the shadows is the following—

Ammonium persulphate	.	2 oz	} or {	32 g	
Water	. . .	25 oz		400 c.c.	
Pure sulphuric acid	.	1 dram		2 c.c.	

When reduction is complete the action can be stopped by placing the negative in a 5 per cent solution of sodium sulphite.

Chromium, being a less vigorous intensifier than mercury-bromide, is advisable if intensification cannot be avoided. The negative is *thoroughly* fixed and washed. It is then bleached in 1 per cent potassium bichromate solution, to which has been added from 1–5 per cent hydrochloric acid. Bleaching should not take longer than two minutes at 65°F. After rinsing, the negative is immersed in 5 per cent sodium carbonate, washed for 10 minutes or so and re-developed in daylight with amidol. Contrast can be controlled by the amount of acid in the bleacher.

The general manipulation of continuous-tone negatives is fully described in the many textbooks which are available dealing with pure photography, and a study of an appropriate selection will be well repaid.

SECTION 3. PROCESS FILMS AND PAPER NEGATIVES

These are frequently used in place of glass plates, particularly for book work, etc., where a large number of negatives are required to be cut to size and "patched up" in position either direct on the glass of a "face down" printing frame or on a separate sheet of glass.

There are several methods of supporting film in the dark-slide, ranging from the use of two sheets of glass to special solutions or fabrics to form a tacky coating on a glass support. Hunter-Penrose Ltd. manufacture a special Film and Paper Negative Holder in the form of either a spring or vacuum pressure frame which fits in the dark-slide, and is so arranged that the sensitive film is brought into the correct focal plane without further adjustment of the back body after focusing. If expenditure permits, the glass front of the frame should be of the best optical quality. This cover glass must be given the same attention and care as a half-tone screen. Dust or marks of any description will be reproduced on every negative, necessitating a considerable amount of time spent in avoidable spotting and retouching.

All the operations described for dry plates apply to the making of film negatives, with the occasional exception of quick drying with spirit and water. Film bases vary in this respect, and the maker's advice must be requested or a trial made. As an alternative to the use of spirit the film may be immersed in a 10 per cent solution of formalin for three or four minutes, rinsed and dried in a current of hot air.

Paper negatives are extremely economical and are being used extensively for line work of all kinds and even coarse screen work. The paper used is specially manufactured for the purpose and is usually sufficiently translucent without further treatment, but, if desired, "white oil," castor oil and turpentine, medicinal paraffin and alcohol or similar combinations may be rubbed on the back and the surplus removed. A "Film Paper," which, as the name implies, is intermediate between paper and film, is a comparatively recent and useful addition to the almost confusingly wide range. Negative paper can be obtained either in rolls of any width up to 42 in. or in cut sheets of standard sizes.

The instructions which are supplied with the paper should be followed carefully, although it is possible to employ the same developer and general treatment as for dry plates. The use of a caustic developer is not advised for standard practice.

An orthochromatic paper is also obtainable which in conjunction with a yellow filter is useful for photographing old and stained originals. The developer recommended by Ilford is as follows—

Metol	. . .	56 gr	3 g
Hydroquinone	. .	$\frac{1}{2}$ oz	12·5 g
Sod. sulphite (cryst.)	.	4 oz	100 g
Sod. carbonate (cryst.)	.	7$\frac{1}{2}$ oz	187·5 g
Pot. bromide	.	16 gr	0·9 g
Water up to	. .	80 oz	2000 c.c.

(with "or" between the two right-hand columns)

With correct exposure, development should be complete in two minutes at 65°F.

Typary & Typon (J. J. Huber) were early specialists in negative paper and film to cover all the requirements of both camera and contact work, and their "Reflex Paper" introduced an interesting process of negative making without use of a camera. The process is of course limited to the production of negatives the same size as the copy. A very wide field of reproduction can, however, be covered, and similar types of paper can now be obtained from all manufacturers.

The only apparatus required is a contact printing frame and a glass or film yellow filter. Supposing the original is a sheet of type matter printed on both sides, or a line sketch on thick card, the procedure is as follows: The yellow filter is placed on the glass of the printing frame and a sheet of sensitive paper is placed on the filter, film uppermost. The copy is laid face down on this. If the original is thin paper printed on both sides it is advisable to place a sheet of black paper over the whole. After contact has been obtained an exposure is made, the duration of which must be ascertained in the first place by trial. The light passes through the sensitive paper and of course has an action over the whole surface, but where light is reflected by the white parts of the copy the light action will be increased sufficiently to produce an image. Normal development and fixing follow. A recommended developer consists of—

Distilled water	.	.	.	.	1000 c.c.
Hydroquinone	.	.	.	.	30 g
Metol .	.	.	.	.	3 g
Sodium sulphite	.	.	.	.	225 g
Pot. carbonate (dried)	.	.	.	225 g
Pot. bromide .	.	.	.	.	30 g

For use take one part of solution and two parts water. Rinse after development, immerse for a few seconds in 3 per cent acetic acid and wash well before fixing. The negative thus produced is not satisfactory for printing down direct to metal, and a contact positive is made on a sheet of the same paper by the usual printing-through method. From this positive the final negative is made in the same manner but using stripping paper or Anti-Halation Celluloid Film. With the former the film can be stripped from the paper support by first trimming the print, loosening the edges by inserting a dull knife and then gently pulling the film away while holding the paper backing on a flat surface. This film is sufficiently tough to withstand normal handling, and being extremely thin it can be printed to metal either face-up or face-down. It is advised that strip films be treated with a weak—say 5 per cent—solution of glycerine and water after washing and without further rinsing hung up to dry in an even temperature. If the film is to be mounted on glass a suitable adhesive is: 40 g gelatine dissolved in 500 c.c. warm water and 50 c.c. glycerine added. Alternatively, use a 3–5 per cent solution of glycerine and best quality isinglass.

The frame used for reflex printing will probably be of the vacuum box type, and as a fairly strong illumination is required this will entail the use of several lamps of approximately 100 watts each. This arrangement means that light will be received by the copy from all angles, and consequently it is most important that a very efficient exhaust equipment is employed to obtain the best possible contact, particularly if the original consists of type which has been reproduced by a fairly heavy impression and the paper indented or embossed.

A suitable apparatus for all types of contact exposures consists of a face-down vacuum frame mounted on a cabinet, the height of which is sufficient to provide even illumination with one central lamp. This type of exposure is essential in practice if the sharpest possible images are to be obtained.

The inside of the cabinet can be painted black to minimize

reflection and maintain to the fullest extent the advantages of parallel rays. Additional white lamps, according to the size of the frame, are positioned on the base, and connected to a separate switch. These are for special purposes where additional "spread" lighting is desirable.

Two ruby lamps are also provided for positioning and register-

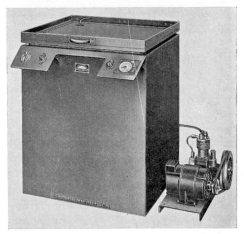

"LITHOTEX" DEEP-ETCH POSITIVE CONTACT CABINET

ing purposes. These are mounted on movable bases in order that they may be positioned directly under the register marks of negatives, and so afford the best facilities with minimum light.

All the switches, including the motor switch, are mounted conveniently on the side of the cabinet. The frame can be supplied with either hand or motor exhaust, and fitted with an automatic timing meter incorporating a mercury switch. This device enables accurate exposures to be made of one-fifth of a second to 60 seconds.

DEEP-ETCH POSITIVE CONTACT CABINETS

Now that the deep-etch process is receiving such a lot of attention, these cabinets are of special interest.

AUTOMATIC CONTACT PRINTING CABINET

The "Lithotex" outfit, shown on page 70, comprises a type of printing cabinet specially designed for the preparation of line and half-tone *composite* positives for deep-etch. Incorporated in this cabinet are a number of features which ensure that a composite positive can be produced from two separate negatives accurately as regards register and with the correct uniform exposure. The outfit is exceedingly easy to operate, consumes hardly any current and is of strong and practical construction.

The Automatic Contact Printing Cabinet

The automatic contact cabinet, recently developed, ensures by its automatic cycle of operations an exact exposure only after absolute contact between negative and sensitive material has been achieved. The cabinet is completely light tight during the exposure and when the lid is released the exposure has already ceased, thereby enabling the operator to leave his unexposed materials uncovered in the dark-room without fear of fogging. Variable sources of illumination can be selected at will, enabling a very wide range of speed of material and density of negative to be catered for.

CHAPTER V

HALF-TONE WITH COLLODION AND DRY PLATES

SECTION 1. SCREEN WORK—WET COLLODION

BEFORE commencing instruction on this subject and in view of the fact that many installations will not include the Diaphragm Indicator, it would be advisable to describe a simple temporary scaling arrangement that can easily be made by the operator.

It has been found by general practice that a diaphragm opening, the diameter of which is $\frac{1}{64}$ of the camera extension, is most suited for the majority of exposures for both line and screen, taking into consideration the covering capacity of the lens and economical exposure times. When the lens opening is maintained at a constant proportion of the camera extension a very obvious advantage arises in that exposure times and screen distance also remain constant for a given type of original and strength of illumination irrespective of the degree of enlargement or reduction. As different subjects require widely varying degrees of enlargement or reduction the camera extension is similarly varying, and to ascertain the required size of stop for any camera extension some method of scaling is necessary.

Having ascertained the required stop it only remains to have a scale on the lens by means of which the aperture can be set accordingly. Assuming that the lens has an iris diaphragm, scribe an arrow on the rotatable control ring in such a position that it will not conflict with the F/numbers. Firmly gum a strip of paper around the lens mount adjacent to the control ring. Unscrew the component of the lens which will allow access to the diaphragm, and with the aid of a pair of dividers set this at, say, $\frac{8}{32}$ in. Mark the gummed strip in line with the arrow on the control ring and number this "8," this figure indicating the diameter of the diaphragm in 32nds of an inch. Successively set the diaphragm at $\frac{12}{32}$ in., $\frac{16}{32}$ in. etc., up to the maximum usable aperture of the lens, marking and numbering the gummed strip at each setting. Each division can be subdivided into four by hand. This calibration permits the lens aperture to be set at any number of 32nds of an inch. As we require a lens opening equal to $\frac{1}{64}$ of the camera extension it is obvious that with an extension of, say, 24 in., the lens opening will be $\frac{24}{64}$ in. (or $\frac{12}{32}$ in.) and the diaphragm being calibrated in 32nds would be set at "12." To simplify operation the camera may be calibrated in divisions or units of 2 in. and the number of these indicated on the scale will be the number at which to set the lens. The camera extension scale can be made as follows—

Set the camera at an extension of an even number of inches, say 24. (For all practical purposes the extension may be considered as being the distance between the lens diaphragm and the focusing screen.) Place a suitable strip of wood along the side of the camera and, with the end butting against the rear of the front body, mark the rod in line with the front of the rear body and number this in accordance with the number of 2 in. units of the camera extension, in this case 12. This starting point once obtained, the rod can be marked and numbered in 2 in. divisions in both directions, the divisions towards the lens reading 11, 10, 9, etc., and those in the opposite direction 13, 14, 15, etc. In use the rod is placed in the original position and the reading nearest the front of the rear body indicates the figure at which the lens diaphragm is to be set.

A spring tape can of course be employed instead of a rod. The container of this would be fixed on the side of the rear body and the free end of the tape to the front body in such a manner that the reading indicated agrees with the measured camera extension. Several inches will have to be cut off the end of the tape for this purpose. As the camera is adjusted for enlarging or reducing, the tape will automatically record the extension in inches; this figure is halved to obtain the lens

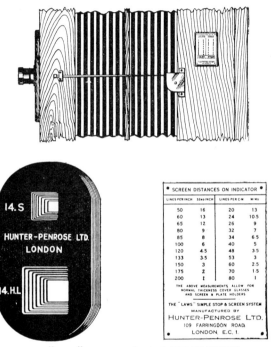

SCREEN DISTANCES ON INDICATOR			
LINES PER INCH	32ND INCH	LINES PER C.M	M.M.S
50	16	20	13
60	13	24	10.5
65	12	26	9
80	9	32	7
85	8	34	6.5
100	6	40	5
120	4.5	48	3.5
133	3.5	53	3
150	3	60	2.5
175	2	70	1.5
200	1	80	1

THE ABOVE MEASUREMENTS ALLOW FOR NORMAL THICKNESS COVER GLASSES AND SCREEN & PLATE HOLDERS

THE "LAWS" SIMPLE STOP & SCREEN SYSTEM
MANUFACTURED BY
HUNTER-PENROSE LTD.
109 FARRINGDON ROAD
LONDON. E.C. 1.

14. S

HUNTER-PENROSE LTD.
LONDON

14. H.L.

THE "LAWS" SIMPLE STOP AND SCREEN SYSTEM

opening in 32nds of an inch. If the metric system is preferred, scale the lens diaphragm in millimetres, set the camera extension at a multiple of 64 mm, say 640 mm, position the rod and number the first measuring point "10." Measure off distances of 64 mm in each direction and number consecutively.

A device which can readily be attached to any camera is the "Laws System." This consists of a series of numbered stops (either square or round) and a spring tape which is secured to the two camera bodies. The tape is specially divided and numbered and the nearest figure recorded at any camera extension indicates the number of the stop to be used. This system is also based on the "$\frac{1}{64}$ ratio."

"Muller" System Diaphragm and Screen-Distance Control

As shown in the illustrations on pp. 77 and 78, this ingenious fitting consists of two parts: a multiple rotating lens scale which works in conjunction with a measuring and calculating drum mounted on the front of the camera. The actual graduations on the multiple scales are obtained after individual optical tests of the lens to which the apparatus is fitted.

Unlike a number of appliances of this character, it is not claimed that this makes process operating automatic, but it is definitely claimed and proved that by the use of this control the quality of the dots is kept constant. The re-toucher will thus receive standard negatives for retouching. By using this control for colour work (for which it was primarily designed) reproofing is reduced and retouching is cut to a minimum, and general economy effected.

This apparatus is hired out annually at a very nominal charge by the manufacturers and patentees, Pictorial Machinery Limited.

In approaching the subject of screen negative making the student should have some idea of what is taking place. However, it is not the object here to discuss all the theoretical details concerned as these have been dealt with at length in the several textbooks available, and a study of these should be made to obtain a thoroughly comprehensive knowledge and understanding of the process as the student becomes more advanced. (See "*Ilford Manual of Process Work*.")

The screen itself consists of two sheets of glass upon which are engraved parallel black lines of a width equal to the spaces between them. (This refers to the standard article; occasionally, screens of slightly different proportions are specified.) The two sheets of glass are cemented together so that the lines cross at

"MULLER" SYSTEM LENS SCALE

right-angles. For photo-litho, the screen most generally used has a ruling of 133 lines per inch, and the "screen angle," or angle of the lines to the sides of the screen, is 45°. (When viewing a half-tone print in the usual way the screen effect is least noticeable when the lines of the image elements or dots are at an angle of 45° to the edge of the paper. To illustrate this effect take a newspaper illustration and view it from one corner. The screen effect immediately becomes more apparent.)

If the screen is placed at a certain distance in front of the plate the subsequent image is split up into a series of dots of varying sizes, the largest corresponding to the whites of the original.

An introductory idea of the control of this effect may be gained by the hypothetical assumption that each of the square apertures formed by the cross lines of the screen acts as a miniature lens making a dot image on the sensitive film which approaches in formation the shape of the camera lens aperture.

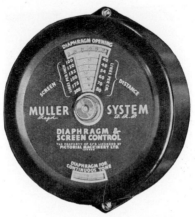

"MULLER" SYSTEM DIAPHRAGM FOR CONTINUOUS TONE

It may also be assumed that each dot is built up from a certain minimum area and increases in size according to the duration of exposure or intensity of light action. The intensity of light varies over the whole screen according to the varying tones of the original, consequently dots are formed on the negative which vary in size as the projected image varies in tone or intensity.

In much the same way as a continuous-tone negative can be controlled regarding maximum and minimum tone rendering, so can the general range of a screen negative be controlled. However, while the former is regulated by varying the scale of *density*, the latter can be controlled by limiting the sizes of the dots, the density of which must remain constant.

The image formation of photo-litho negatives should range from a very small dense dot in the clear portions corresponding to the black parts of the original, to a practically unbroken or non-printing deposit in those parts representing the whites.

The degree of contrast or scale of gradation obtainable from any given copy is controllable to a very great extent; the mechanical factors governing this control and the general structure of the dot formation are as follows—

Camera extension, screen ruling, screen distance, lens aperture.

There is a definite relationship between these factors which enables a standardized system to be adopted resulting in negatives of uniform quality and gradation irrespective of the degree of enlargement or reduction, or the difference in scale of gradation of the average range of subjects. The camera extension and screen ruling are fixed and known factors for any given conditions, and consequently govern the two adjustable factors of screen distance and lens aperture according to the system employed. The $1:64$ ratio is now generally accepted, which means that for the starting point of the system the lens aperture will be $\frac{1}{64}$ the camera extension (ascertained and set by means of the camera scale and diaphragm indicator), and the screen distance 64 times the screen opening. The screen opening is the distance between the engraved lines, which in the case of a 133-line screen is $\frac{1}{266}$ in. This multiplied by 64 is approximately $\frac{1}{4}$ in. and the screen gear is set to give this distance. Similarly,

for a 100-line screen the distance would be $\frac{1}{200} \times \frac{64}{1} = \frac{1}{3}$ in.,

or in millimetres: $\frac{1}{3} \times \frac{25 \cdot 4}{1} = 8 \cdot 4$ mm. The screen distance

for normal operation will remain practically constant for any degree of enlargment or reduction.

The gear for supporting and positioning the screen should be of a strong and rigid design to ensure absolute precision of adjustment, and parallelism between screen and plate. If the scale records the distance between the surface of the screen and the plate surface, due allowance must be made for the thickness of the cover glass, for the term "screen distance" always implies the distance between the lines of the screen and the plate surface.

The student may perhaps be disconcerted by seeing experienced operators ignoring these standardized methods and attempting to approach the same results by utilizing only two or three series of stops for all camera extensions and then judging the screen distance by racking the screen until the dots formed on the focusing screen acquire a certain "draught-board" formation known by experience to be correct. This further entails the estimation of exposure for every degree of enlargement or reduction, and the guesswork thus imposed encourages reliance upon after-manipulation to correct, with doubtful success, the faults which are bound to occur periodically. There is quite enough judgment required on account of varying qualities of originals without ignoring the definite assistance which is afforded by systematized control of mechanical and optical factors. A system forms a basis upon which modifications necessitated by varying types of copy can be estimated to a fine and constant degree, with the result that the best possible negatives are obtained with assurance.

It is invariably necessary to employ more than one stop during the exposure, but as it is desired to proceed along experimental lines which will give a better indication of the process, the first trial exposure will be with one stop aperture only. (See pp. 43 and 81.)

Select a copy such as an unretouched contrasty bromide print with good blacks and clear high-lights. Place the half-tone screen in position and focus the image to a convenient size. To facilitate focusing, a sheet of type matter could be placed on the board at the side of the copy. Examination of the image with or without a magnifying glass is mostly a matter of personal preference. Adjust the screen gear so that when the screen is racked into position it will have a screen distance of $\frac{8}{32}$ in. (For screens other than 133-line ascertain the correct distance as described.) Referring to the camera scale, set the lens aperture at the figure recorded for $\frac{1}{64}$ the camera extension.

Coat and sensitize a plate in the normal manner and position in the dark-slide. When this is attached to the camera and the slide opened, adjust the screen and make an exposure the duration of which will be some seven or eight times that required for a line subject with the same illumination, say three minutes. Develop for the normal time as described for line work, wash, and fix in cyanide solution. There is no need to intensify the negative for present purposes, but if it is desired to obtain more readily comparable results the copper and silver intensification may be given. The image examined through a magnifying glass will show a dot formation covering only a limited portion of the full tone scale. Whether this portion is at the bottom of the scale or towards the top will depend on the exposure given. In other words, if the exposure has been short the parts of the negative representing the blacks and near blacks of the copy might be entirely clear glass, the exposure being insufficient to overcome the inertia of the sensitive film; and the whites of the copy would be represented by isolated dots or square-shaped dots just touching at the corners. An over-exposure would possibly have still less variation between the high-light and the shadow portions, but the general density of the whole image would be increased, the shadow dots being large and well defined and the high-lights consisting of large squares joined up or overlapping at the corners. A second negative can now be made with an estimated exposure to render the deepest shadows as a very small dot on clear glass. Should this negative be intensified and printed on metal the lightest tones of the print would be much too heavy and the detail in the shadows would probably be lost, that is, the three-quarter tones as well as the blacks of the copy would be reproduced as solid black owing to the lack of density in the shadow dots rendering them ineffective. However, the exposure for this negative is taken as a basis and will be considered as the main exposure. If the copy has no intense blacks it is probable that the shadow dots will have sufficient density, but we will assume that scale correction is required here. For this purpose a "flash exposure" is made. This is a short supplementary exposure usually to a piece of white paper held over the copy. It is common practice to use a smaller aperture for this purpose, but careful tests fail to indicate any advantage and a stop about half the diameter of the main or "detail" stop is advised.

The exposure to white paper or, alternatively, a diffused bank of illumination should only be sufficient to make a small dense deposit in the centre of each dot, and so give effective density to the shadow dots which would otherwise be too weak. With the average original the duration will be about 10 per cent that of the main exposure. A prolonged flash exposure results in a flattening of the shadows. Sometimes an opal metal filament lamp is held very close to the lens aperture and a flash exposure given. Some later designs of cameras feature a "flashing unit."

The lower scale of gradation having been corrected, the high-lights and first tones must be given attention. It has been previously stated that the high-lights of the negative should have no printing value: to obtain this result and at the same time maintain the correct tone rendering elsewhere has given rise to many and varying methods of procedure. The most common of these is the use of a large square stop for an additional exposure. The area of this is usually about twice that of the "64th" stop, and it has the effect of closing up the high-light formation, the exposure having more effect on the eventual printing quality of these parts of the negative than on the shadows.

The relative duration of this exposure depends on the type of original and the consequent degree of contrast which has to be obtained by photographic means. About 10 per cent of the main exposure may be taken as a basis. If the ratio can be reduced, so much the better, for the methods necessarily employed to increase general contrast have the tendency to impair the sharp definition of the dots themselves.

The after-treatment of the negative is the same as described for line work using copper, silver, iodine and sodium sulphide. Reducing with weak cyanide after iodine is an important part of the process, as it can often be used to great advantage for opening out isolated portions of the negative and so strengthening the print at these places. Such local reduction must be carried out very carefully and critically, using a still weaker solution than would be used for general clearing or reduction. A drop or two of the solution may be applied repeatedly with a pointed wad of wool or a soft camel-hair brush and immediately washed away; or the negative may be held under running water in such a position that a smooth stream passes over the surface of the film, and the solution can be applied by dropping from cotton-wool from a height of three or four inches. If local reduction becomes a feature of frequent practice owing to the nature of originals, considerable help would be afforded by the provision of a large bottle with an outlet at the bottom to which is attached a thin flexible rubber tube with spring clip and terminating in a pointed glass tube. The bottle is placed on a shelf above the sink and the reducing solution with which it is filled should always be made up to a definite strength, say, one part of a 10 per cent stock solution to 100 parts of water; the two must be thoroughly mixed. The negative should be placed on a stand

and under running water when applying the reducer as above. A good overhead light is essential.

SECTION 2.   FURTHER CONTROL OF DOT FORMATION

While it is advisable to keep the screen at the correct distance, it is possible, within certain limits, to vary the general constrast of a negative by varying the screen distance: an increase of screen distance gives greater contrast, and a decrease, lesser contrast.   On no account must the screen distance be changed while making a negative.

A very useful aid to the production of good high-light negatives is the special diaphragm incorporated in the Penray "Hilite" Lens.   This consists of a double cross-shaped stop aperture, the arms of which can be adjusted for width and length. An indicator shows the size of the openings equivalent to $F/32$, $F/45$, and $F/64$.   This diaphragm, together with the iris diaphragm, provides an extremely effective and positive control of the formation of the screen image.

Stops of almost every conceivable shape have been employed from time to time, their users claiming special advantages for each.   With the majority, however, the net result is no better than can be obtained with stops of one of the recognized types, of which the most generally employed are the square stop and the square stop with extended corners.   The latter with the addition of a small hole situated a short distance from the middle of one side has a certain advantage particularly when a number of varying types of copy have to be photographed on one plate. The result is a negative of good average quality which has, perhaps, an increased latitude of manipulation when printing down to metal.

A very useful adjustable square stop is now available.   This can be set to any size within its limits and rotated to any angle. It fits in the usual slot provided for Waterhouse stops.

A type of subject which, perhaps, causes more trouble than others in the production of good high-light negatives is a pencil sketch including light delicate tones. The retention of these together with full high-light effects is a matter for careful adjustment of the high-light exposure. If a slightly longer exposure than normal with the square stop or square stop

THE PENRAY "HILITE" LENS, SHOWING ONE
ARRANGEMENT OF THE SPECIAL STOP

with extended corners does not give the required result, instead of increasing the exposure time it is advisable to employ a still larger stop, the length of the sides being, say, twice the diameter of the 64th stop. This exposure may either take the place of, or be supplementary to, the normal high-light exposure.

An extended use of high-light stops in order to increase contrast results in a faint spreading of the shadow dots, but providing these have been well formed by the main and flash exposures the surrounding fringe of weak density can be cut away with the cyanide reducer after iodine treatment.

A method of high-light negative making sometimes adopted is a supplementary exposure through plain glass after the screen has been removed. As this necessitates the removal of the dark-slide and its replacement (except with cameras built specially for the purpose), it is essential that the construction will ensure correct register. The exposure made through the plain glass is

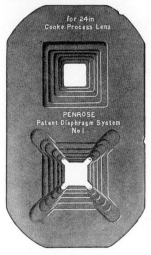

SET OF HALF-TONE STOPS

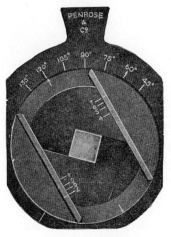

ADJUSTABLE DIAPHRAGM
(SMITH'S PATENT)

only sufficient to form a slight veil over the high-light portions, and this has the effect of retarding light action when printing on metal.

Considerable correction and improvement can be made by careful painting-out with opaque or dye, but it is a serious and unfortunately common mistake to rely too much on this work to overcome faults of exposure. The best possible negative must be made in the first place and then just a light touch of colour applied to those parts of the negative which have not correctly "high-lighted" owing to a discoloured or otherwise poor original. If the negative as a whole is too flat and then the required high-lights painted out, the print will be hopelessly distorted, for the light tones will be much too heavy and will jump from a strong grey to pure white with none of the light tone detail which is so essential.

SECTION 3. IRREGULAR GRAIN NEGATIVES

The use of a grain structure instead of the regular half-tone formation is often employed effectively, and can be used as an aid in reproducing originals which already consist of half-tone dots. The Erwin screen is a typical example. It consists of a special reticulated gelatine film on a glass support, and depends for its action on diffraction effects. The screen has to be placed very close to the sensitive plate, and exposure for a normal negative is made with one stop only. General contrast may be increased or decreased by varying the screen distance as in ordinary half-tone procedure, but for the majority of photo-litho work the separation afforded by the thickness of the cover glass is sufficient, and contrast variations are obtained by development control. The appearance of the printed image is similar to that obtained with the metzograph screen with which many operators will be familiar. If using dry plates the film may be reduced or intensified as usual, but this will increase the general contrast.

Another irregular breaking up of the image which periodically finds favour among advertisers is the "canvas effect" which is obtained by employing a sheet of rather irregular wire gauze, bolting silk, etc. This is placed between two sheets of glass and used as a half-tone screen, employing more or less the same methods of determining the screen distance, lens aperture and exposure as with engraved screens. The printed result is more effective if the "screen" is placed at an angle of

90°. Hunter-Penrose Ltd. supply special screens for this class of work.

SECTION 4. DRY-PLATE SCREEN NEGATIVES

The use of dry plates for screen work is becoming increasingly popular, particularly when large numbers of medium-sized negatives are required, and where speed of production compensates for the extra initial cost.

The principles governing the dot formation are of course the same as described for wet collodion, but the negative image must consist of dots covering a different scale of gradation. This is again on account of the image being built *in* the film instead of on the surface, and, further, the dots have not quite the same abrupt stencil-like change from density to clear film which is a feature of wet collodion. Although certain types of modern process plates are manufactured with an extremely thin emulsion to minimize this effect, there is often an appreciable "spread" of light when printing down, particularly if the printing lamp is of the multi-arc type, or if two or more lamps are employed. (Such printing conditions arise from the necessity of evenly illuminating large areas.) The dry-plate image structure must therefore be of a nature which will allow for this spreading, and exposures regulated in order that the dots are of sufficient size to maintain the shadow detail according to type of emulsion and printing conditions. Careful co-operation between the metal printing department and the studio will enable the operator to arrive at a decision regarding the standard scale of gradation towards which he must aim. With an entirely new department care must be taken that the final decision in this respect is not premature, for there are several factors influencing the print on metal from a given negative which are not at first appreciated, and the effect of these might lead to condemning a type of negative which is really satisfactory. As a general standard, however, a "direct" camera negative may be considered as suitable for average printing conditions if the shadow dots are of full density and about one-third the linear size of dots just touching at the corners (using a 133-line screen), and with the high-lights almost closed up but not quite to the extent necessary with wet collodion. A dry-plate negative has a slight veil between the high-light dots which becomes effective to a degree governed by the total amount of printing exposure required by the negative as a whole, and the type of illuminant. This veil is more pronounced in a negative which has had to be excessively "high-lighted" in order to obtain standard contrast from a flat original. When dealing with a reduced and intensified negative from which much of the fringe and veil surrounding the dots has been removed, conditions are more nearly approaching those of wet collodion negatives and the shadow dots should be smaller and the high-lights of a closer formation. A rather common fault is the production of negatives in which there is a tendency for the image to be built up partly by the varying size of the dots and partly by a varying density. This is principally due to under-development; even if the negative has been inadvertently over-exposed, the development should be full in order to obtain the maximum contrast between the dense dots and clear film.

The dry-plate negative lends itself to local hand correction as described later, but this—with black and white work—should only be necessary when dealing with faulty copies which cannot be retouched in the first place.

Since the foregoing was written for the first edition of this work, a considerable improvement has been effected in the thin film type of process plate, resulting in emulsions which produce much sharper image elements with an extremely steep gradation from opacity to clear film. "Light spread" is consequently lessened to a considerable extent, as also is the necessity for reduction and intensification of negatives. The instructions throughout, however, are being retained in the original form, for even with the latest facilities there is a tendency for the effects mentioned to develop under certain conditions, This possibility must be kept in view and the same precautions taken in avoiding them will still further ensure the best possible results with improved materials. It must further be borne in mind that negatives with a slight graded dot effect using the thicker type of emulsion are often employed purposely to facilitate retouching by chemical methods.

It was stated earlier that it is invariably necessary to employ more than one stop during the exposure; although this procedure is generally adopted it can often be modified considerably, and in point of fact there is much to be said for the use of one stop only. Assuming, for instance, an original is reasonably bright and of good contrast, it will be found, particularly with the present dry-plate emulsions, that if the exposure is long enough an adequate dot formation can be obtained in the shadows without recourse to a flash exposure.

Such an exposure without compensating adjustment would, however, cause the high-light to be over-exposed and result in excessive contrast. This contrast can be avoided by using a smaller stop and retaining standard screen distance, or reducing screen distance and retaining the normal stop. The author prefers the former, keeping the screen distance at 64 times the screen opening and using a stop approximately $\frac{1}{90}$ the camera extension. This produces sharp and dense dots of excellent printing quality, and greater or less general contrast, according to the requirements of the original and its reproduction, can be obtained by a small adjustment of screen distance.

It will, of course, be realized that if an entirely satisfactory dot structure can be obtained without use of a flash exposure the negative will reproduce all the tone values with the least possible flattening of the reproduction curve, particularly at the lower end of the scale. Further, if the stop used to obtain this effect is somewhat smaller than is indicated by the "64th" ratio coupled with no increase in screen distance, the dots throughout the full range will be of added sharpness yet possessing adequate "core" for reduction purposes.

CHAPTER VI

COMBINED LINE AND TONE

SECTION 1. STRIPPING AND TINTS

STRIPPING is an operation whereby the photographic film is removed from its original support and either used as an unsupported film or transferred to a new surface. The process has many applications and is particularly useful for composite line and screen work, or where several negatives are required on one plate, the subjects requiring individual treatment regarding exposure or degree of reduction or enlargement.

Reversal of the image can also be obtained by "double stripping" in cases where a prism is not available.

The wet collodion film can be stripped very readily and there are several methods of procedure, the two most common being as follows—

1. The glass upon which the negative is to be made is thoroughly cleaned as usual, but the albumen substratum is omitted. When dry, the surface is polished with a soft rag and a little French chalk, all trace of this being finally removed with a clean camel-hair dusting brush. In place of the albumen substratum a margin of rubber solution (or sometimes egg albumen solution) is painted around the glass to a depth of about half an inch, this being sufficient to secure the film during the subsequent manipulations. The completed negative must not be coated with any protecting solution, but when dry is flowed over with a thin solution of rubber and naphtha which when set is followed with a coating of stripping collodion. This is better purchased specially made for the purpose, but plain collodion can be used by the addition of one part of castor oil

to approximately 120 parts of collodion. When this is beginning to set at the bottom corner the film should be "fired" by applying a light to one corner. This not only saves time but gives a better result. Care must be taken that this operation is carried out in a suitable part of the room.

The rubber forms a protection against the solvent action which would otherwise occur between the stripping collodion and the negative collodion film, and must be sufficiently thick to prevent subsequent cracking but not so thick that water will not penetrate.

The portion of the negative to be removed is cut around with a sharp knife and the film soaked in 5 per cent or 10 per cent glacial acetic acid until it commences to lift. The plate is removed from the acid bath and it will be found that by starting at one corner the film can readily be lifted from its support and is sufficiently tough and flexible to withstand reasonable handling. A small pool of gum solution or fish glue is spread over the new support and the stripped film manœuvred into position, then squeegeed down, preferably with a piece of paper placed over the film. If the negative is required as a film it may be stripped on to oiled paper and another piece of oiled paper squeegeed on top for storing purposes.

2. This method is simpler and quicker, but requires very much more careful handling.

The negative is made on substratumed glass and completed in the normal manner. When quite dry the portion to be removed is cut around and after a short wash a stripping solution is carefully applied until the film starts to loosen. This solution consists of one part sodium fluoride, one part hydrochloric acid and 40 parts water. The acid should be added immediately before use. After loosening the film it must be washed very gently, and this is best done by using a measure and allowing the water to flow on to the centre of the film. If the plate were placed under a tap the film would probably disappear down the sink. A moistened piece of bank paper or special paper supplied for the purpose is squeegeed on to the film and raised again, bringing the film with it after starting from one corner.

Should the film start to tear owing to a particle of dirt on the glass or a pitted surface, the film should be laid down again and the stripping recommenced from an opposite corner.

"Double stripping" is necessary if reversal is required. The stripped film is transferred to a second sheet of moistened paper before finally positioning on the gummed new support.

Dry plates may also be stripped by cutting as required and applying the following stripping solution—

Sodium fluoride	.	.	.	$\frac{1}{4}$ oz			10 g
Formaline	.	.	.	2 oz	or		80 c.c.
Water	.	.	.	5 oz			200 c.c.

When the film has loosened, it is rinsed and with the aid of a piece of moistened paper it can be lifted, reversed if necessary, and transferred to the new support. Only a very weak gum solution need be used as an adhesive, but this should have a few drops of glycerine added.

The film will be tougher and less liable to distortion if it is first soaked in a 10 per cent solution of formaline for several minutes; or the film may be coated with stripping collodion. In the latter case it will be found that a longer application of the stripping solution will be necessary.

The use of fluoric acid is particularly quick and sure, but it is a very dangerous acid to keep and use in the studio. The fumes attack glass readily, and much damage can follow the least carelessness. However, if due precautions are taken and the operations are carried out in a room where no harm will result, the following method can be recommended—

After cutting the dried film, it is soaked in full-strength formaline for five minutes, rinsed and blotted. The plate is then placed in a 10 per cent solution of formaline to each ounce of which has been added 7 or 8 drops of fluoric acid. The solution may be applied locally with a brush if it is desired to retain the remaining portions of the negative. The film will be seen to loosen from its support in 15 to 20 seconds and is then carefully washed. If the film has completely lost adhesion to the plate, the water will have to be gently poured over from a measure. A piece of moistened paper is squeegeed over the film which can then be removed and transferred as above. If the formaline treatment has not been entirely effective the film might stretch either as a whole or in part. The application of methylated spirit and water will cause the gelatine to shrink again, but it is better of course to give careful and precise manipulation throughout and so avoid stretch and blisters.

Dry plates can be stripped in the dry condition by immersing the dried negative for one minute in—

Pot. carbonate	.	.	.	1 oz			20 g
Glycerine .	.	.	.	½ oz	or		10 c.c.
Formaline	.	.	.	½ oz			10 c.c.
Water	.	.	.	25 oz			500 c.c.

Remove the surface solution with a soft chamois leather and allow to dry, when the film can be cut and stripped from one corner.

Special dry plates, films, and negative papers are available which can be stripped immediately after drying without any special manipulation. Ilford offer the following instructions regarding their stripping plates—

These plates should be processed and dried in the normal manner. To enable them to strip, the emulsion should be cut round with a sharp knife or scalpel and the corner turned up. Either the whole plate or small pieces may be stripped.

Retouching or blocking out should be done before stripping.

The following method of affixing pieces of film removed from stripping plates to another piece of glass or to a negative has been found to be extremely effective.

Having stripped the piece of film it is desired to transfer, damp the glass where the film is to be put with methylated spirit. Place the film on the glass and manœuvre into position with the point of a penknife.

When in place, hold securely in position and wash it over with plain water, using a camel-hair brush. The strokes should be firm and in one direction only.

The film will now adhere quite firmly.

To the foregoing may be added the necessary precaution to keep the film entirely free from moisture before and while positioning with spirit, and the final application of water must be completed as quickly as possible.

The use of a stripping solution even with stripping plates has been found very beneficial, particularly with large negatives. The carbonate-formaline-glycerine solution will be found most suitable and will greatly assist in the prevention of distortion during stripping and transferring.

A new type of stripping film recently introduced comprises a strong paper base with a thin sensitive film which, after the usual photographic manipulation, can be stripped from the support while still wet and without any fear of distortion or shrinkage. The wet film can be mounted on a new support, either glass or celluloid, face-up or face-down, and mostly without the use of any applied adhesive. The film is very tough, and in consequence can be handled with ease, and exact fitting in composite jobs is rendered particularly simple. If desired, heat may be applied to hasten drying, which can be completed in two or three minutes.

When composite. ine and screen negatives have to be made using separate originals, much trouble is avoided by "blacking out," with dull black paint or black paper, those portions of the line copy which will subsequently be occupied by screen work. This of course results in a clear film on the line negative ready to receive the stripped film. If this is not practicable and the unwanted film has to be removed from the large negative, the whole of the portion concerned need not necessarily be scraped away, which is an exceedingly laborious proceeding. Instead, cut a margin $\frac{1}{8}$ in. or so wide and apply stripping solution with a suitable brush, taking care that no solution spreads beyond the margin. The loosened film is then readily removed and the glass cleaned and dried.

It is an advantage to coat the negative with stripping collodion and so protect the cut edges from moisture when positioning the stripped film, or if this latter has been "dry stripped" or dried after stripping it may be squeegeed down to the coating of stripping collodion, which if not too dry will be sufficiently tacky to obviate the use of adhesive. With some makes of "strip film" it is necessary to moisten the film after positioning it in this manner.

When cutting the film prior to stripping, the accuracy required will depend on the job, and if exact fitting is essential, a tracing is taken of the appropriate portion of the large negative and fitted over the film to be stripped, when both paper and film can be cut through with the required accuracy.

The many uses of stripping will become obvious when considering the problems which are presented by contact with various classes of commercial work, but one might be mentioned here with advantage, and that is the application of the process to take the place of tint laying. If part of a subject has to receive a line or dot tint this is usually added by the accepted litho methods after the plate has received the photographic image. This is frequently far from satisfactory and entails much unnecessary work, particularly if the plate includes several repeat designs. If, as occurs with many designs, the tint can be photoprinted, the results will be far superior and time will be saved not only in the production of the tint (in the case of repeat work) but in the after-treatment of the plate, which, if hand work is present, takes considerably longer than for an entirely photo-printed plate. If a selection of collodion tint negatives is prepared at times when the camera is not otherwise engaged these could be kept in readiness for stripping as occasion arises; or if the rubber-collodion method is employed, the films could be stripped and dried immediately, then stored between smooth paper. Various strengths of half-tone tints can be made by use of the screen, giving different exposures to white paper; also line tints by using a line stop at exactly the same angle as the lines of the screen. This stop may be about the same width as F/64 and about six times as long. Similarly, a cross tint can be made with a cross-shaped stop of the same dimensions. If difficulty is experienced in obtaining perfectly straight lines a narrow line or cross aperture about $\frac{1}{16}$ in. $\times$ 2 in. may be cut in thin card and this is secured to the lens board in place of the lens. The angle of the aperture must be exactly the same as the lines of the screen: the relative position can be noted by observing the diffraction effect when looking through the screen (preferably with the focusing screen removed). A series of overlapping images will appear as an extension of the main cross or line of light and the stop must be rotated until these are in exact alignment. The screen distance must be adjusted while examining the projected image on the focusing screen with a magnifier.

Stipple tints will have to be photographed from impressions made with shading mediums on dull enamel paper. Enlargements or reductions from these impressions give a further range of textures.

If the whole of a line subject is to be broken by a line or screen tint the foregoing suggestions regarding single and cross-line effects can be applied as follows—

The line copy is focused and a normal exposure made,

followed by a second exposure to white paper but with the screen in position, and a single line, cross or round stop, according to the required tint, placed in the lens. If only a portion of the subject is to be broken with line or stipple, a piece of the previously prepared film can quickly be positioned on the negative.

SECTION 2. ZIP-A-TONE

When a line original requires tints added, either as a black pattern on the whites or white stipple, etc., on solids, the usual method of using shading mediums on the negative or litho plate is now being replaced by use of the *Zip-a*-Tone process which enables impressions in black or white dry ink to be transferred to the copy. This allows the effect to be judged before photographing and, if necessary, the tint can easily be removed and replaced with a different pattern without injury to the copy. Two or more impressions can be superimposed, giving a very wide variety of textures and strengths.

The process employs sheets of specially prepared transparent paper on which are transferable ink tints. These are applied to the copy simply by laying the *Zip-a*-Tone sheet in position, rubbing down with a suitable burnisher, applying water with a brush or cotton-wool and stripping off the transparent paper support. As adhesion of the pattern requires both burnishing and damping, much scraping for high-lights and around the edges of the design can be obviated by painting out the back of the *Zip-a*-Tone sheet where required with a waterproof liquid after rubbing down. When the sheet is subsequently removed the pattern will adhere only where it has not been painted out. Similarly, if the detail has been followed when rubbing down using a soft pencil or similar burnisher and then the whole moistened, the pattern will be transferred only where burnished.

CHAPTER VII

COLOUR REPRODUCTION METHODS

SECTION 1. COLOUR WORK

THE principle of three-colour printing is based on the fact that for reasonably accurate colour rendering three pigments, each reflecting approximately one-third of the visible spectrum, when superimposed in the correct proportions will reproduce any given hue.

An approach to the ideal of true colour rendering might be afforded by superimposing three positive images on gelatine, each image of a colour comprising a third of the visible spectrum. Providing that the images agree in intensity, the result as viewed by transmitted light would be a good visual replica of the subject. However, such ideal conditions do not occur in printing.

The pigments used in three-colour work—yellow, rose pink and blue green (usually spoken of as tricolour yellow, red and blue)—are not transparent and do not present on the printed sheet their full intensity, nor reflect the exact part of the spectrum desired. Consequently the resultant combined value does not agree with the theoretical value. Hand work on negatives or plate and over-emphasis of the first printing help to balance matters, but additional printings are usually given in order to overcome the defects due not only to the limitations of pigment printing and dot structure of the image, but to the variations in value often imposed by the necessary methods of obtaining the printing plate. The extra printings usually consist of one or more of the following: black, grey, light blue, pink and some-times a special rich or brilliant colour which is better obtained by a separate printing than by an attempted combination of two or more of the normal colours to secure the desired effect.

For the present we shall consider work in four printings for which four colour-separated screen negatives have to be prepared on special plates which are sensitive to light of all colours, or, to be more exact, to the whole visible spectrum, though to slightly varying degrees. These plates are called "Panchromatic." If each of the four plates were made with the same screen angle the resulting print would show a very pronounced pattern effect or moiré. This effect can be observed to an extreme degree when two screen negatives are placed face to face. It may also be noticed that the pattern reaches a minimum when the two screen rulings are in a certain relative position. In the same manner the moiré pattern of a print is minimized by employing screen angles which vary one to the other. Three half-tone screens are usually specified: these are ruled at angles of 45°, 75° and 90°. The 75° screen upon reversal gives an angle of 15°. The allocation of colours to angles is not a matter for a definite ruling beyond stating that the most prominent colour, usually the blue, is printed with the 45° screen. The common arrangement is yellow 15°, red, 75°, blue 45°, and black 90°.

In place of the three separate screens one circular screen is frequently employed but this very seriously limits the maximum size of rectangular negative which can be made in any given size of camera. This limitation is of no importance where a camera has to be provided for much larger line work than the size of screen work contemplated. In such circumstances the circular screen is a considerable economy.

The colour separation is obtained by photographing through colour filters, which, as the name implies, filter or "cut-out" certain colours. These filters can be thin layers of gelatine in a thin metal rim, for insertion in the lens stop aperture, or a gelatine layer sandwiched between two optical flats, and it is obvious that these must be of the finest material and most careful manufacture if the definition of the lens is not to be impaired and perfect register maintained. The extreme care which has to be taken in the selection of the glass, the optical surfacing, lengthy drying, testing and general production of the filters, renders those of the highest quality an expensive item, but with reasonable care they will last a great number of years. It is not generally realized that the same critical attention is required for making a perfect set of filters as for a highest-quality lens, and the same care should be accorded them regarding cleaning and storing, particular attention being given that they are not allowed to get over-warm or damp.

It is advised that books such as "The Photography of Coloured Objects," published by Kodak Ltd., and "Panchromatism," published by Ilford Ltd., be studied; but for a working conception of colour separation the following will probably suffice—

The filters for tri-colour work are commonly referred to as blue, red, and green, but each covers or transmits a wider band of the spectrum than the name suggests. For the production of a negative recording any particular colour the appropriate filter passes all effective light radiations from the subject which it is desired *not* to print, and this light produces a deposit of varying density, the clearer portions of the film thus being a printing record or negative record of the colour which has been "held back" by the filter. For example, supposing it is required to obtain a negative in which the clearer portions are to represent the yellow printing, a filter must be used which is photographically complementary to our sensation of yellow. Such a filter is the blue-violet and it has the effect of converting to black and grey all parts of the copy which will be reproduced with a yellow pigment.

Similarly for the red printing a green filter is used, and for the blue printing a red filter. For the black or grey printing a

filter is employed which will produce a negative record of the
visual *luminosity* of the subject, or in other words as we should
record the full range of colours in tones of grey, such as in a
wash drawing. The filter for this purpose is of a yellow or light
green-yellow appearance (Ilford "Gamma" or Kodak "K3").

ROTARY SCREEN CARRIER
For attachment to the ordinary Screen Gear.

In practice the black-printing negative does not require to be
such a complete record, and modifications are made which will
be described later.

The use of a filter naturally increases exposure time and
each has a definite and individual multiplying factor, or a
constant by which a known exposure time without a filter must
be multiplied. That is, to obtain a set of negatives of the
correct relative value, a varying length of exposure has to be

given for each plate according to the filter used. The multiplying factor of each filter varies according to the type of illuminant. In each box of panchromatic plates should be found a table giving the approximate multiplying factors for each filter with several types of illumination. It is essential, however, to regard

COLOUR FILTER HOLDER AND PRESERVING BOX

this table only as a guide, and tests should be made under existing conditions before commencing work. It may seem a superfluous remark, but it must be remembered that the figures on the published charts do not refer to actual exposure times but represent the amount by which unity must be multiplied, unity being the exposure time for any given set of conditions but without the use of a colour filter.

A satisfactory test can be carried out as follows, using small plates, say, $6\frac{1}{2}$ in. $\times$ $4\frac{3}{4}$ in.: Cut an aperture 3 in. $\times$ $\frac{1}{2}$ in. in the centre of a 6 in. × 12 in. card and at right angles to the longer side. Place the card in the screen holder with the aperture vertical and a graded strip of neutral grey and black (which can be obtained from the plate makers or a supply house) on the copy-board, and adjust for focus and position. The panchromatic plate is positioned in the dark-slide a couple of inches or so to the right of centre and a short exposure made which is carefully timed to, say, three seconds. Take the slide into the dark-room and move the plate half an inch to the left. Now place the yellow filter in position and make an exposure, the duration of which will be ascertained by reference to the table. For instance, supposing the multiplying factor for the yellow filter is given as "4" and the first exposure was three seconds, twelve seconds will have to be given. Proceed as above for each of the remaining filters, giving carefully timed exposures according to the table. It is advised that the arc lamps be switched on a minute or so previous to each exposure so that any variation of light intensity due to lamp fluctuation is minimized. If the developed plate presents a series of strips of identical densities, the maker's table of multiplying factors will have been verified as correct for the existing conditions. However, in many cases it will be found that the strips are far from identical and a second negative must be made with estimated variations in exposure time where necessary in order to obtain a series of equal-density strips. Several attempts may be found necessary before this is accomplished, but the time spent is well worth while.

An apparently correct series of multiplying factors having been found, these should be verified by two or three further negatives to eliminate the possibility of results being affected by arc lamp fluctuations. (This introduces a variable quantity which can only be controlled for critical work by special means, such as the photo-electric exposure meters now available from leading supply houses.)

Supposing that the times for the final negative read as follows—

Without filter (or unity), 3 seconds; yellow filter, 12 seconds; blue filter, 21 seconds; green filter, 31 seconds; red filter, 12 seconds; the test has shown that multiplying factors for the filters are as follows: yellow 4, blue 7, green $10\frac{1}{2}$, and red 4. (The ascertained correct exposure divided by "unity" gives the multiplying factor for each filter.) The table will be altered accordingly and these figures will remain constant as long as conditions do not alter. The plate-makers' tables should of course be examined from time to time to note any variations in manufacture which may occur. Modern plates, however, appear to have no variation of emulsion sensitivity in this respect from year to year.

The several methods of obtaining colour-separated screen negatives fall into two general classifications known as "direct" and "indirect"; the former refers to screen negatives made direct from the original with the appropriate colour filter in position, and the latter infers the use of continuous-tone colour-separated negatives, from which are made positives of some description and finally screen negatives. Each method has its own pros and cons, and the choice of method to be employed is to a great extent dependent on the nature of the work in hand, subsequent methods of printing down, permissible cost, and personal preference and skill of the staff. A few points for consideration are as follows—

Direct method: One negative only for each colour with consequent saving of studio costs; no loss of detail beyond that imposed by the screen; more difficult to retouch owing to the necessity of both additive and subtractive retouching; more critical printing-down manipulation.

Indirect method: Greater facilities for hand correction and additions or alterations; possibility of employing wet collodion for the final negatives, thus permitting a length of exposure when printing down which will give an added assurance of absolute insolubility and thorough hardening of the albumen image; allows the making of several identical final negatives for certain methods of duplicate printing down when mechanical devices are not available; large screen negatives can be made from comparatively small continuous-tone negatives, and varying sizes of screen negatives can be made from one set of retouched continuous-tone positives; similarly, enlarged negatives of coarse screen ruling from fine screen positives; additional cost in time and material; possible loss of detail but minimized according to the skill of the photographer. The indirect method becomes a necessity for the reproduction of pictures or articles which will not permit the use of a screen camera equipment when photographing the original.

SECTION 2. DIRECT COLOUR-SEPARATED NEGATIVES

Before making a serious attempt at colour work the student should accustom himself to the handling of process panchromatic plates. As these are sensitive to all colours it is obvious that no safe-light is effective to a degree comparable with those used for ordinary plates. Unpacking the box, loading the dark-slide, and development should preferably be carried out in complete darkness. The plates being least sensitive to green, a dark green safe-light may be employed to enable the position of some mislaid article to be found, but the lamp should only be switched on when absolutely necessary. If proper care is taken beforehand in positioning the several utensils in the natural sequence of use, and the operator learns to adjust the plate in the dark-slide, etc., by touch alone, he will quickly accustom himself to what at first might appear a difficult operation. In any case the permissible amount of light is of little aid when first entering the dark-room from a lighted studio.

As correct development can be governed by time and temperature, the natural temptation to watch the formation of the image must be ignored. A dark-room clock of the type which gives an audible warning after the stipulated time is of course essential. Attempting to count the period or instructing an apprentice to "bang on the door in three minutes" is obviously a dangerous and often disastrous economy.

The developer should be as instructed by the makers; they invariably recommend hydroquinone-caustic, and times of approximately 3 minutes at 60°F, $2\frac{1}{4}$ minutes at 65°F, or $1\frac{3}{4}$ minutes at 70°F. The temperature should be tested carefully and precautions taken to maintain this at a definite degree throughout the production of a colour set.

In the previous section a method was suggested of ascertaining the correct multiplying factors governing the several filters. The next step in direct colour work is to ascertain "unity," that is, the exposure or series of exposures which will produce a good screen negative from a given type of copy using panchromatic plates but without a filter. Small plates can be used for this purpose and the work will assist in giving the operator the necessary practice in working without a dark-room lamp.

The reader is referred to the chapters dealing with screen negatives in wet collodion and dry plates. Working on similar lines, i.e. with proportionate stops and screen distance and a known lamp distance, an exposure is made with screen and stop adjusted according to the scale. Several trials will have to be made before a negative of the desired dot formation and gradation is obtained. Previous experience in black and white work with dry plate or film will indicate the results required and the method of obtaining them. It is quite possible that an exposure with one stop ($\frac{1}{64}$ camera extension) together with a short "flash" will prove adequate. Even if a supplementary high-light exposure is found desirable, this need rarely be made with a square or extended corner stop, the larger round stop of, say, $1\frac{1}{2}$ times the diameter of the main stop being usually quite sufficient. If, however, due to individual preference or special circumstances, a square stop is employed in the following colour work, care must be taken that the diagonals are at the same angle as the screen ruling. Special stops can be obtained which can be partly rotated in the Waterhouse slot of the lens, otherwise the lens itself has to be rotated either on a special mounting or on its screw thread. The latter might appear a dangerous procedure, but does not have appreciable consequences in practice.

Having ascertained by trial that the correct and standard exposure for a panchromatic plate without filter is, say, 3 seconds flash (using stop $\frac{1}{2}$ diameter of main stop), 12 seconds with main stop ($\frac{1}{64}$ camera extension), and 2 seconds with the high-light stop ($1\frac{1}{2}$ times the diameter of the main stop), these exposures will be considered as unity for all subsequent colour work with the same type of original. It is understood of course that the previously described stop system is employed throughout.

Before placing the coloured sketch on the board, a register mark must be placed in the middle of each end or in such positions as will facilitate future manipulations of the negative in the printing frame. A small tab should also be placed at the side with the name of the colour about to be photographed clearly marked, in order to avoid possible confusion later. A colour chart serves a similar purpose but is less likely to avoid confusion when including negatives for special printings. It is a decided advantage to place a graded strip at the side of the copy; the strip being of neutral greys and blacks should record the same densities on each negative and affords a much more definite guide for comparison than the pictorial images. Further, any variation due to one-colour photographing with more or less contrast can readily be noted for future if not immediate correction. After focusing the image to correct size, the camera must be securely locked, special devices being provided for this purpose.

Assuming that the common screen angles are to be employed and the first negative is to be the yellow printer, a screen with a 15° ruling is positioned in the holder (this angle is sometimes called 105°). When focusing the image it is of the utmost importance that a filter is placed in position—a "dummy," if one is available, or else the green filter. If the latter, it will be found necessary to open the diaphragm almost to its full extent in order to obtain a sufficiently brilliant image for accurate focusing. The undesirability of this practice is not so noticeable here as in critical line work. (See page 36.)

The blue filter is now placed in position ready for exposure of the yellow-printing negative. Referring to the corrected or verified table of multiplying factors it is found that the blue filter increases exposure, say, 7 times; therefore with the assumed unity values of 3 seconds flash, 12 seconds main, and 2 seconds high-light, the exposure through the blue filter will be 21 seconds flash, 84 seconds main, and 14 seconds high-light. As, however, there is no need to have the filter in position when making the flash exposure, this will be the same for each negative, i.e. 3 seconds.

Development follows according to time and temperature, then thorough fixation. The dark-room lamp may be switched on after a minute or so of fixing. The immersion should continue for a period at least equal to that required for apparent fixation. (A fresh plate may be placed in the dark-slide during this operation and preferably before switching on the lamp.)

If the previous tests have been carried out carefully and the standardized methods adhered to, the negative should have the same density and dot formation or general printing quality as had been found correct for earlier dry-plate negatives made for black and white work.

Should there be any doubt regarding constant strength of illumination, it is always better to over-expose rather than run the risk of an under-exposure. A considerable over-exposure (providing that development has been complete) can be corrected by subsequent reduction or clearing without impairing the quality or gradation of the image. In any case it is advisable to be able to reduce the negative slightly with weak ferricyanide and hypo: this will help to clear some of the veil which always occurs around the dots. Intensification must be avoided at this stage in view of the methods of hand correction to follow.

Constant strength of illumination must not be taken for granted. Variation due to poor condition or type of arc lamp is often very noticeable. If, after taking every precaution to ensure that the lamps are working at their best, they still cause variation, it is advisable to make a practice of switching on shortly before an exposure rather than start an exposure when the lamp is about to re-feed. Voltage fluctuation of the supply mains cannot readily be corrected and the inclusion of a voltmeter or ammeter in the circuit is a considerable aid as an indication of the necessity to depart from standard exposures.

Modern standards and production methods rely upon an exposure which represents a quantity of light action, rather than a time recording. Exposures are made by pressing a button to open a shutter, which concludes the exposure by closing only after a pre-determined amount of light has passed to the plate. If the illumination decreases, the photo electric meter prolongs automatically the duration of the exposure, and a sudden over brilliance from the lamps causes the exposure period to be cut down.

If the red-printing negative is made next, the screen is reversed back to front to obtain the required angle of 75°, the green filter placed in position and the reference tab altered. Again referring to the assumed table of multiplying factors it is found that the green filter necessitates an exposure, say, 10½ times unity. The red plate exposure will thus be 3 seconds flash (as unity on account of no filter), 126 seconds main, and 21 seconds high-light.

Do not attempt to use the quantity of developer that was used for the first plate unless full experience has been gained regarding the working of this type of developer, and to what extent or after what interval it may be used. It is much safer at all times to use fresh developer for each plate, and check the temperature before using.

The blue-printing negative is made with a screen angle of 45° and the red filter (multiplying factor 4), the exposure being 3 seconds flash, without filter, 48 seconds main, and 8 seconds high-light: the black-printing negative—screen angle 90°, yellow or green-yellow filter (multiplying factor 4), 3 seconds flash, without filter, 48 seconds main, and 8 seconds high-light.

It must be remembered that all the above times are of necessity quite suppositional and based on an assumed test.

Modifications: As the yellow is printed first and it is known that the following colours are not of the maximum transparency, it is advisable to make the yellow negative slightly more "open" than standard. This of course is preferably effected during the retouching operations, but a little extra general reduction may be carried out by the operator. The decision will have to follow the experience of the department in connexion with similar work, inks and paper. There is a tendency for the blue filter to produce somewhat flatter negatives, and this tendency can be corrected by giving slightly longer development in the case of continuous tones, or more high-light exposure for direct screen negatives.

The black-printing negative may also be modified to reduce the amount of retouching required. Usually a negative of more general contrast is required with the lightest tones brought to a high-light. This is accomplished by slightly increasing the supplementary exposure with the large round or square stop.

This completes the photography of a four-colour set and the plates after thorough washing are sent to the artists' department for hand correction.

SECTION 3. DIRECT SIX- OR SEVEN-COLOUR WORK

When additional printings are considered justifiable, the four negatives are made as described above but with the exception that those having a corresponding tint are made with a little more contrast either by increasing the screen distance, or preferably by increasing the proportion of high-light exposure.

The tint negatives require to be considerably more "open" and flat by comparison. As an example take the production of a negative for the light blue: the screen angle will be the same as for the normal blue—45°—and the red filter used. The suggested exposure for the blue negative was 3 seconds flash, 48 seconds main, and 8 seconds high-light, with a screen distance of 6 mm. The screen distance is now reduced to 5 mm., the flash given as normally, and the main exposure reduced slightly, say by 10 per cent. No high-light exposure need be given. This will produce a negative with a clear printable dot over the whole film. Quite broad retouching is all that will be required for the average subject when dealing with light tints. The exposures for pink, grey, etc., will have the same relationship to the standard exposures for red, black, etc.

Negatives for special colours such as brilliant green or violet are usually only required for isolated parts of the reproduction and not employed for general construction of the image. The common practice is to make a blue negative for green or violet, etc., or a yellow negative for orange, flesh, etc., and paint out or correct where necessary. Complementary filters can be obtained for a great variety of colours, but they are rarely used in commercial practice. Two tri-colour filters are occasionally utilized for the production of one negative. For instance, an orange-printing negative is required and this is to incorporate considerable detail: the colour might be considered as a combination of two-thirds yellow and one-third red, consequently the negative would be given two-thirds the normal exposure of a yellow-printing negative and one-third the normal exposure of a red-printing negative. The foregoing should be considered an expedient rather than theoretically correct procedure.

The manufacturers of Barnet Plates have introduced an extra green sensitive panchromatic plate, which has been specially prepared to shorten the rather long exposure usually required when using the green filter. This plate is approximately $2\frac{1}{2}$ times faster under the green filter than the standard plate, and gives a good, clean, solid dot.

SECTION 4. INDIRECT COLOUR-SEPARATED NEGATIVES

More variation in the practice of *indirect* colour work will perhaps be found than in any other section of photo-lithography, and it is difficult to claim any one method as being the best to adopt as standard practice for all conditions and classes of work.

The process as a whole is being superseded in many houses by the direct method, in view of the present better understanding of dry-plate screen negative making and retouching, and the obvious economy of time and money. Also there is the increasing use of deep etch and bimetal processes, requiring the print on metal to be made from retouched half-tone positives, the photographic operations thus falling between direct and indirect negative making.

Admittedly there is much in favour of some form of the indirect process, and though perhaps the extra expense may not be considered justifiable for general adoption, there are frequent cases where it becomes more than a matter of choice and effects a definite eventual economy, or is an actual necessity.

The generally accepted procedure is described in the following.

The usual register marks are first placed on the copy, and the reference colour tab and graded strip at the side. Continuous-tone negatives are made for the required number of colours excluding tints. (The exclusion of special negatives for tints is not always considered expedient.) "Process Panchromatic" or "Rapid Panchromatic" plates are used, the latter being about twice the speed of the former. Exposures will become standardized after ascertaining by trial and error the correct exposure for a plate made without a colour filter and then applying the multiplying factors which have been corrected as previously described.

The plates are developed, using a formula which will give a full range of tones. Time and temperature are of still greater importance here than with screen negatives, for after-treatment is not applicable to the same degree and would be likely to cause serious loss of relative tone values.

A suitable developer will be found in each box of plates, the following being typical—

Stock pyro solution

	Pyrogallic acid .	.	.	4	oz	} or {	40 g
	Pot. metabisulphite	.	.	1	oz		10 g
	Water to .	.	.	40	oz		400 c.c.
A.	Stock pyro solution .	.	.	2	oz	} or {	20 c.c.
	Water	.	.	18	oz		180 c.c.
B.	Sodium carbonate	.	.	2	oz	} or {	20 g
	Sodium sulphite	.	.	2	oz		20 g
	Pot. bromide 10% solution		¼	oz		2·5 c.c.
	Water to .	.	.	20	oz		200 c.c.

For use mix equal parts of A and B.

A similar developer containing acetic acid is sometimes preferred—

A.	Pyrogallic acid	. . 1 oz			25 g
	Acetic acid .	. . 45 minims	} or	{	3 c.c.
	Sodium sulphite	. . 4 oz			100 g
	Water . .	. . 20 oz			500 c.c.
B.	Sodium carbonate .	. 2 oz	} or	{	50 g
	Water . .	. 20 oz			500 c.c.

For use take one part each of A and B and four parts of water. The degree of contrast can be considerably varied by increasing or reducing the quantity of water or the proportion of pyro.

The precautions regarding dark-room illumination— or rather lack of it—are of still greater importance when dealing with continuous-tone, for any light fog, which would certainly be irregular, would eventually be recorded as an actual enlargement of the dots in the final negative. For the same reason the slightest stain is most dangerous and every care must be taken that the plate is rocked during development and an ample quantity of developer used; the plate must be well rinsed after developing and completely immersed in an acid fixing bath and remain in the solution for several minutes after fixation is apparently complete, then washed thoroughly and dried. Drying may be speeded up by immersing the negative in spirit for a few minutes, but spontaneous drying is to be preferred if time allows.

Retouching the negative is dealt with in a following section, but it might be mentioned here that with this particular method only pencilling or similar means of increasing density is required on these negatives.

Glass positives are next made from the negatives, either by contact in a pressure frame or in the camera using a transparency attachment. If the former method, the pressure frame should always be positioned at a constant distance from the source of light (see page 69). Backed plates preferably are used, and these may be either "Fine grain ordinary" or "Process": with the latter a longer exposure and softer or diluted developer will be found essential to prevent increased contrast. If backed plates are not available a solution of gum arabic and lamp-black may

ALL–IRON CAMERA STAND FITTED WITH METAL TRANSPARENCY
ATTACHMENT

be painted on and allowed to dry in racks in the dark-room. If required before dry, a sheet of paper should be placed over the backing to prevent it adhering to the frame cover. Exposure will have to be found by trial in the first place until the estimated correct density and gradation is obtained in the development time stipulated by the makers, say, three minutes at 65°F.

If a transparency attachment is used, either through preference or the advisability of enlarging at this stage, it must be examined carefully and any necessary steps taken with worn equipment to ensure that the negatives will each be positioned in exactly

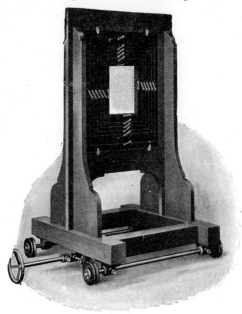

"UNIVERSAL" DETACHABLE TRANSPARENCY HOLDER

the same plane, otherwise variations in size will occur in the following positives or final screen negatives. The best of modern camera stands are fitted with metal transparency holders built to the rear of the copy-board which has a removable centre portion of the required size. This type of holder is constructed on similar lines to the metal screen holder and ensures absolute and permanent accuracy. With this model the lamps are swung round to illuminate a reflecting roller blind or a sheet of white paper or card suspended about three feet behind the negative. Another model consists of a wooden frame with a series of adapters to suit all standard-size negatives within the limits of the equipment. This frame can be securely attached to the camera stand at any suitable distance from the copy-board, to which is fastened a reflecting sheet. The relative positions of the transparency holder, reflecting surface, and lamps should always be constant in the interest of standardization.

Normally the negatives will be placed with the film towards the lens. No appreciable amount of light must be allowed to fall on the face of the film. Some equipments are fitted with special bellows or curtains to ensure these conditions, but simple masking can be quite effective. The position of the arc lamps must be given attention in order that direct reflection of the arcs from the reflecting white paper does not cause uneven illumination; also that light from the arcs does not fall direct on the negative or lens.

If the plates are backed by the operator there is no necessity to wait for these to dry; they may be placed straight in the dark-slide after painting. The backing, by the way, should be washed off before developing.

Extra positives are preferably made according to the number of tints required. Each of these of course will be made from the negative of the corresponding full colour—light blue from blue negative, pink from red negative, etc. The type of positive suitable for the tints can be obtained by increasing the exposure 50 per cent or more and diluting the developer. This will result in a much stronger but flatter positive. While it is not absolutely necessary to make these tint positives because of the possibility of making two final screen negatives from one positive, it will be found the better practice on account of greater latitude in retouching.

The positives are retouched and strengthened where necessary, then one is secured in the transparency holder and with the half-tone screen of the required angle in position the image is focused to the correct size. The camera is locked and a screen negative made either by wet collodion or dry plate.

The expensiveness of large dry plates makes it more economical to produce medium or small-size colour-separated continuous tone negatives, and to use wet plates or "ordinary" dry plates for enlarged positives or screen negatives.

The standard stop system is used although the exposure time and proportions will be slightly different from those when photographing direct from a monochrome sketch. However, once the exposure or series of exposures to produce the required high-light negative has been ascertained it will remain effectively constant for all future negatives; but a slight decrease of exposure will be found necessary when making a considerable reduction in size. An allowance must also be made to avoid an increase of contrast beyond that anticipated. It should not be necessary, however, to include a flash exposure when working from transparencies.

Each of the negatives should be made with the same exposure if the full set of positives has been correctly photographed and retouched. If however one positive has to serve for two colour printings of the same description, then the final negatives must be modified accordingly—one normal, or with just a slight increase of contrast for the strong colour, and one much flatter and open for the tint.

The final screen negatives should only require spotting and painting out in the larger areas of high-light film before being sent to the printing-down department.

It is strongly advised that the student undertakes some monochrome work by the indirect method before attempting the added complications of colour reproduction. By so doing he will be able to judge with much more accuracy the density and scale of gradation which is most suitable throughout.

The use of wet collodion for continuous-tone positives is still favoured in a few studios, particularly in America. When dealing with large reproductions the saving in cost as against large dry plates no doubt accounts in a great measure for its retention. Grained glass prepared in the lithographic graining machine, or etched glass, is employed to facilitate retouching.

A source of constant trouble with this process is the dirt and particles of old film which adhere so tenaciously to the rough surface. The glass plates should be well soaked in the acid bath followed by vigorous scrubbing and cleaning with pumice powder and hard rag.

Standard negative collodion is mostly used, but the best results are perhaps more readily obtained with a "Positive Collodion." Coating and sensitizing is normal, using a silver bath of 30–35 gr to the ounce (7–8 g per 100 c.c.), or a rather stronger bath, say 10 per cent, which can be slightly alkaline. The first exposure will have to be found by trial. After normal iron development the film is well washed and fixed (preferably with hypo), again washed and blackened with a solution of sodium sulphide, approx. 5 per cent.

The process of redevelopment can be employed with advantage as it allows greater latitude of manipulation.

The following stock solutions are made—

A.	Pyrogallic acid	.	.	.	$\frac{1}{4}$ oz	}	or	{	5 g
	Citric acid	.	.	.	$\frac{1}{2}$ oz				10 g
	Distilled water	.	.	. 20	oz				400 c.c.
B.	Silver nitrate	.	.	.	$\frac{1}{2}$ oz	}	or	{	10 g
	Distilled water	.	.	. 20	oz				400 c.c.

Equal parts of A and B to be mixed immediately before use.

If the developed plate appears to have sufficient contrast and is only lacking in density, it may be redeveloped by repeated applications of the pyro-silver solution before fixing. When both contrast and density are to be increased the plate is fixed and washed first. If found advisable the plate may be redeveloped both before and after fixing. The solution must not be poured repeatedly on one portion of the plate unless local intensification is definitely required.

If a stain should occur after prolonged treatment a weak solution of acetic acid will mostly provide a remedy.

The final result should be a film ranging from a maximum density which is slightly translucent, to practically clear glass.

STUDIO REGISTERING GAUGE

After the film has dried spontaneously or by application of heat, the image can be easily retouched, using fairly soft pencils, charcoal stumps, etc.

When working with a transparency attachment, trouble is sometimes experienced with incorrect registration on account of inferior mechanical or optical equipment. Negatives and positives should be tested carefully with a "register gauge stick" or one plate of a set may be placed film to film with each of the others in turn and any variation in distance between register marks noted. If the trouble is persistent and cannot be overcome immediately by obvious means, a rather laborious and critical testing and correction in the making of the final negatives will be necessary until the cause is located and rectified. Two methods are suggested as follows—

1. Remove the plate limiting the movement of the dark-slide

shutter and slide this out of the grooves. Place the dark-slide on the camera with the first negative in such a position that the lower register mark coincides with that of the second image; side movement of the negative and adjustment of the rise and fall mechanism of the lens board enable this to be done with the required accuracy. Careful note of the coincidence or otherwise of the upper register marks will show whether any correction of size is necessary. If so, adjustments must be made on the *front body only*. Much more adjustment than will be found necessary could be made here without seriously impairing the definition. Each of the following images must be tested in the same way before making exposures, unless it is known that variation occurs in one colour only: the negative for this would of course be left to the last.

Use of the screen makes sighting rather difficult, and the second method will be found easier in this respect—

2. Two small pieces of thin tin-foil shaped like a wedge with the points cut off are moistened and positioned point to point on the inner face of the focusing glass at a carefully measured and checked separation, the separation being the distance between the register marks of the first screen negative, or projected image of the first positive. By manipulation of the lens board control, part of the lower register mark of each succeeding projected image can be made to coincide with the top of the tin-foil. Alignment of the upper register mark and tin-foil can be corrected if necessary by adjustment of the front body only for alteration of size, and adjustment of the rise and fall gear to maintain alignment of the lower register mark.

The above two suggestions are assuming that the copy is placed with the register marks in a vertical line; should they be in a horizontal line the rise and fall adjustments will be replaced by sliding the copy-board to left or right. This will necessitate the services of a helper and the minute adjustments required will be found considerably more difficult unless some form of screw adjustment can be improvised.

If there is the slightest doubt regarding perfect register of the dark-slide and focusing screen it would be better, in place of the latter, to use a sheet of etched glass in the dark-slide, the shutter of which has been removed.

When variations of size occur during the making of colour-separated negatives, there are two possible causes to be examined apart from mechanical defects or inadvertent movement of the camera. The optical equipment may not be fully corrected: this will be evidenced by the same variation in size occurring with every negative taken through any particular colour filter. The second reason, and one which is frequently overlooked, is shrinkage of the sketch while on the copy-board. With large originals and negatives this shrinkage can be very noticeable. Sketches are often left in a comparatively damp part of the studio overnight and then placed on the copy-board, quickly focused and the first negative made. As the heat of the arc lamps takes effect the sketch starts to shrink and a progressive variation in size occurs with each negative.

Departments reproducing large maps, etc., are fully alive to this trouble and extreme precautions are always taken that identical conditions prevail at each operation. The first precaution where trouble has been experienced is to ensure that the original is thoroughly dry before making any negatives, and it would be advisable to check the size of the copy with a studio registering gauge (*not* a strip of marked paper or card) before each exposure.

SECTION 5. VARIOUS INDIRECT METHODS

1. A variation of the basic method described in the previous section is the use of screen positives instead of leaving the screen to the production of the final negatives. This affects the retouching

principally, the photographic operations being fairly obvious. Continuous-tone colour-separated negatives are made as required: these are placed in the transparency holder and screen positives made which in this case must be of the correct size for reproduction unless it is proposed to obtain final negatives with a different screen ruling. Normally the final screen negatives are made on Backed Process plates with a very steep gradation by contact in a pressure frame or by placing film to film in the dark-slide and exposing to white paper through a small lens aperture.

This method is being increasingly favoured owing primarily to the realization that the greater part of necessary colour correction consists of reduction of the recorded values. This work is most readily carried out by chemical reduction of the positive. Furthermore, dots which have been produced by photography through the half-tone screen (as opposed to exposure by contact) can be made with excessive silver deposit or density in the centre and a gradual lessening of density towards the periphery. This feature of dot construction is to be avoided in other circumstances but is of considerable advantage to the retoucher, and in fact makes dot reduction a practical possibility.

When using a spring pressure frame for contact printing the source of light must be as far as convenient from the frame, and as an aid to minimizing reflection from walls, etc., the lamp could be enclosed in a box with a small aperture covered with frosted or opal glass. A dark-room lamp with a suitably cut strawboard to take the place of the safe-light serves the purpose quite well. For extremely critical and large work of this description the difficulty of obtaining a perfectly even illumination over a large area can be overcome by providing a small hole in the roof of the studio if the situation renders this feasible, or else in the upper part of the black window covering; arrangements must of course be made to prevent direct sunlight entering.

Mention has been made of final screen negatives of a different ruling to the positive. This might be necessary when for certain classes of poster or large show-card it is desired to print with a screen ruling of, say, 65 lines to the inch. If the only screen available is ruled at 133 lines per inch, the size of the positive must bear the same proportion to the final negative as 65 to 133, i.e. slightly under one-half. For example, if a negative 24 in. × 20 in. is required with a ruling of 100 lines per inch, using a screen of 133 lines, the positive would be made three-quarters full size—18 in. in length. This is placed in the transparency holder and an enlarged wet collodion negative made. Extra care in focusing will of course be necessary, using a stop for the purpose only slightly larger than will be used for the actual exposure.

2. Particularly in view of present methods of retouching and familiarity with screen work, there are certain advantages in commencing with colour-separated screen negatives instead of continuous tone: the same type of plate (regarding contrast) can be used throughout, and with the same treatment. It is not necessary to make quite such a contrasty or high-lighted negative as is required for immediate printing on metal, consequently a crisp and well-defined dot formation is more easily obtained; the methods of retouching can be confined almost entirely to chemical operations and the inexperienced artist is less likely to spend unnecessary time in working up the small detail which is apparent in a continuous-tone negative but which is inevitably lost in the finished screen reproduction (to a degree dependent on the screen ruling). Exposure is not so extremely critical, for over-exposed negatives if correctly developed can be reduced without serious loss of relative values. The general procedure will be obvious from what has already been described, the only point to be commented upon being the fact that general contrast tends to increase slightly at each operation and allowance

must be made accordingly by reducing the high-light exposure and increasing the main exposure to compensate, where necessary; or reducing the size of the main stop (where high-light exposure had not been given previously) and increasing exposure time; or decreasing the screen distance, giving exposure with the main stop and flash only.

3. The combination of continuous-tone negatives, bromide prints, and final screen negatives is occasionally employed but with doubtful success, particularly with colour work, owing to the lack of register which is bound to occur through distortion of the paper (unless this is mounted on gelatine-coated glass) and the difficulty of obtaining even and consistent values on the several bromide prints. Also there is the difficulty of matching the medium used for retouching so that it has the correct photographic value in relation to the print. Anyone who has attempted partly retouching a bromide print previous to re-photographing will appreciate this point. The method has its applications but principally in connexion with small work, and mention of it is made more as an answer to previous and possibly future inquiries as to "Why not?" than as a practical suggestion.

4. A method retaining considerable popularity on the continent employs photography only to a limited extent: this consists of printing screen negatives to stone and colour correcting by lithographic drawing and etching, finally pulling ink impressions and transferring to metal.

5. Process engravers who have an occasional demand for small photo-litho plates find the following rather useful though decidedly expensive. Colour screen negatives are printed to zinc or copper and "fine-etched" in the accustomed manner. The interstices between the dots are filled in by rubbing over with chalk or magnesia and if necessary the plate is given a light rolling with black ink using a glazed roller. The plates can then be

used as originals and "line" negatives made by wet collodion after focusing.

6. A method of producing very fine results has been evolved and patented by Mr. Th. Kirsten, of Leipzig. Briefly the method consists in making colour-separated negatives, printing these to metal or stone, pulling black impressions on suitable card using an offset proof press, retouching these impressions and making final screen negatives by the wet collodion process or dry plates. This of course entails the making of screen negatives from a copy already principally composed of screen dots, and a pronounced moiré pattern would be anticipated. The effect is prevented by the use of special stops throughout in conjunction with the screen angles of the final negatives varying 30 degrees to those of the impressions.

The stops are shaped to produce an oval or elongated dot (more pronounced in the middle tones). A suitable shape is an elongated hexagon, the two longer sides having a small triangular portion cut away from the centre. A series of different size stops are made to conform to the requirements of a standardized stop system.

As different screen angles are used the lens will have to be rotated in order to bring the longest diagonal of the stop in line with the screen angle, or several series of stops could be made.

Colour-separated negatives of normal printing contrast are made and roughly retouched, then printed to stone or metal. These prints are treated lithographically and impressions pulled on the offset proof press, using black or occasionally grey ink. The paper or card must be of the best quality, slightly matt surface, good photographic white and thoroughly seasoned.

The artist will find these impressions particularly suitable for all degrees of correction and alteration and extremely easy to work on, using black or white powdered chalk applied with stumps, cotton-wool, etc., these alterations being easily erased or modified if applied too heavily. The white powder clings to the ink dots, reducing their value to the required degree, while black powder fills the spaces between the dots. Correction by brush, charcoal, crayon, pencil or pen can also be effected with ease.

In addition, modifications may be made in the manner of pulling the impressions. For instance, a double impression may be given with a lightly rolled plate to increase the general contrast, or a plate may be heavily inked with a grey ink to obtain a flatter impression suitable for a tint record.

Finally each retouched impression consisting of both screen elements and continuous-tone hand work is re-photographed with the screen at an angle varying 30° to that of the impression. The same stops are used as previously, and this assists in the prevention of moiré effect. The stops are turned to correspond with the screen angle.

If a flash or supplementary exposure with a smaller stop is found advisable, round stops may be used. This also applies to the first negatives.

There have been numerous processes associated with the present subject which have been brought forward (and sometimes marketed) from time to time with varying commercial success. Many of them are quite satisfactory in the hands of their inventors or those with an enthusiasm for the idea, but workshop practice is a stringent critic and not too ready to absorb suggestions which do not immediately prove a saving in cost or an improvement in quality—though mostly willing to try a thing once, providing that too much expenditure is not involved.

Few of these sometimes revolutionary ideas survive to be accepted by the trade as a whole, for nowadays any departure from standard practice has to meet the approval not only of the "office" and costing department but of the practical and knowledgeable worker.

Progress is bound to occur, however, and regarding immediate considerations one of the first requirements is a new method of making screen positives or negatives by contact or projection, the essentials being cheapness, speed, the production of absolutely clean-cut dots, and the possibility of rapid and fool-proof enlargement or reduction of the screen elements at any period and by localized hand work or staging.

A preparation called Neokol made by the F. Wesel Manufacturing Co. of New York appears to be a step in the right direction. This is a light-sensitive solution which can be coated on glass, exposed and developed, leaving a sharply-defined image which can be "staged" and further developed or etched as required.

Several patents have been granted regarding similar preparations or along similar lines, but none appears to conform to the requirements just presented.

A. C. Austin suggests the following method of making contact negatives or positives. Take any process plate, expose to white light and develop until the film is practically opaque. Rinse and dry. Any number of plates can be so prepared. When required for use immerse for five minutes in 3 per cent ammonium bichromate. Rinse very quickly and place in a dark drying cupboard. When dry make a contact exposure using for preference a single-arc lamp at about five feet. Exposure will have to be ascertained by trial. Immerse in a strong reducing bath such as ferricyanide and hypo, or cyanide and iodine, until the parts unaffected by the arc lamp exposure are reduced to clear film. After washing and drying, the film is ready for local correction by the usual means.

A frequently useful and cheap method of making contact positives is by means of chemicals always at hand as follows—

A flat sheet of glass is thoroughly cleaned and coated with

$2\frac{1}{2}$ per cent ammonium bichromate solution (neutralized with ammonia) 6 oz, fish glue 1 oz. The plate is whirled dry, particular attention being given to avoid dust, over-heating, light fog or incomplete drying. The back of the glass is painted with a mixture of lamp-black, water, and glycerine or any plate-backing paint. Whenever possible a single-arc is used for exposure, the actual time being ascertained by trial. Frequently it is advisable to expose sufficiently to enable development to be completed by gentle rubbing with cotton-wool. After exposure the plate is rinsed and immersed for 30 seconds in a 5–10 per cent solution of methyl violet dye and washed under running water until the image is perfectly clear. The plate is intensified by immersion in lead nitrate 4 parts, potassium ferricyanide 5 parts, water 80 parts, followed by washing and blackening with diluted ammonium sulphide (not sodium sulphide). The effect of this is at first scarcely apparent, and a second and sometimes a third application of the intensifying solutions is necessary. When dry the plate can be rubbed over with cotton-wool to remove any loose deposit and then given a protective coating of clear cellulose varnish.

SECTION 6. COLLODION EMULSION

The emulsion developed by Freundorfer has been extensively used for both colour and black and white. This emulsion enables users to make their own plates as with wet collodion, but no silver bath is required and the plates are dried before use; consequently a number can be prepared in advance of requirements. The plates can be rendered colour sensitive, etched, and intensified by any of the standard methods used for wet or dry plates, are suitable for both direct screen and continuous-tone work, and with screen work the dot formation is of the stencil-like quality which assists the printer on metal to such a great extent. Full instructions are supplied to users, but the following

will be sufficient for an operator experienced in standard wet-
and dry-plate methods—

Thoroughly clean the glass in 10 per cent nitric acid and coat
with a substratum of gelatine (1) or albumen (2) and dry in a
dustproof cabinet.

No. 1

Gelatine	.	.	. 45 gr	or	3 g	
Distilled water	.	.	. 36 oz		1 litre	

This is warmed sufficiently to melt the gelatine and then 2 oz.
(or 50 c.c.) of 2 per cent solution chrome alum added. Filter
while still warm.

No. 2

A. Egg albumen crystals . ½ oz ⎱ or ⎱ 16 g
   Distilled water . . . 30 oz ⎰   ⎰ 1 litre

B. Chrome alum . . . 20 gr ⎫   ⎧ 1·5 g
   Water . . . . ½ oz ⎬ or ⎨ 16 c.c.
   Dissolve and add   ⎪   ⎪
   Formalin . . . . ¼ oz ⎭   ⎩ 8 c.c.

Pour B into A and allow to stand until precipitation stops
and filter.

Sensitized Coating Solution

The completely sensitized plate consists of a coating of
emulsion, the light sensitivity of which is increased by flowing
over one of three "coating solutions," according to the type of
negative required. The "red coating" is used for line negatives,
black and white half-tones, yellow-printing negatives (with
violet filter), and red-printing negatives (with green filter). The
"blue coating" is used for blue-printing negatives (with red
filter), and the "black coating" is used for the black-printing
negative (with a light yellow filter or in certain cases no filter

at all). The coating solutions are prepared before use, as follows—

RED COATING

To each 100 c.c. add 5 c.c. sensitizer. The speed of the emulsion is increased by using a larger quantity of sensitizer up to a maximum of say 10 c.c. More than this may cause fog.

BLUE COATING

To each 100 c.c. add 2 c.c. of sensitizer (more than this will not increase the speed).

BLACK COATING

To each 100 c.c. add 2 c.c. sensitizer (if it is desired to increase the sensitiveness to green and blue, 3 c.c. should be added).

Preparing and Sensitizing the Plates

Red-coated Plates. Before coating any plates, the emulsion must be thoroughly shaken for two or three minutes until all precipitated silver bromide has disappeared. With a ruby safelight in the dark-room lantern the plate is coated with raw emulsion in the same manner as for wet collodion, taking particular care to rock the plate to avoid markings. After the emulsion has set for about 30 seconds, the red coating is applied at the thick corner of the emulsion, and allowed to flow (*without stopping*) from one end of the plate to the other two or three times. The surplus is returned to the bottle from the thick corner, and then the plate rocked with the thick end uppermost for 30 seconds or so, and placed in an absolutely light-tight drying box in a vertical position. An air space of approximately 3 in. should be allowed between plates to ensure even drying.

Blue and Black Coating. These plates are prepared in the same manner, but special care must be taken regarding the use of a green safelight, as these plates are sensitive to all colours.

When large plates have to be coated, operations can be

simplified by flowing over the following solution and draining before applying the colour coating—

Glycerine	.	.	.	3 oz	or	100 c.c.
Distilled water	.	.	.	6 oz		200 c.c.
Industrial alcohol	.	.	1 pint		700 c.c.

Before exposure the plates should be allowed to dry for 15 to 20 minutes, according to temperature. Insufficient drying will cause too much contrast, and possibly dots which are not of maximum sharpness.

Actual exposure times cannot be given, but first trials can be based on a rating of H and D 25.

Trial exposures for colour work can be based on those required for process panchromatic plates, taking a multiplying factor of 6 for the standard green, red, and blue filters. and 4 or less for the yellow filter, using open type arcs. If a filter is used for the black-printing plate, it will usually be found satisfactory to use a yellow filter lighter than normal, with consequently less exposure.

Development

CONCENTRATED DEVELOPER

Potassium carbonate	.	.	1 lb	or	400 g
Sodium sulphite (crystals)	.	1 lb		400 g
Water	.	.	.	40 oz		1 litre
Hydroquinone	.	.	.	1 oz		25 g
Glycin	.	.	.	¼ oz		6 g
Ammonium bromide	.	1 oz		25 g

For use, take one part of concentrated developer to ten parts of water; fresh developer should be used for each plate.

FIXING SOLUTION

Hypo	.	.	.	1 lb	or	400 g
Potassium metabisulphite	.	1 oz		25 g
Water	.	.	.	40 oz		1 litre

After exposure the plate is washed under the tap for a few seconds, allowing as little light as possible to fall on the surface. Development beyond 2 minutes at 65°F tends to produce dots with weak edges. Special care must be taken with the blue- and black-coated plates regarding dark-room illumination, and if possible they should be washed and developed in darkness. A ruby safelight can be employed during manipulation of the red-coated plate.

Reducing and Intensifying

Any of the methods commonly in use for collodion or dry plates can be employed, according to the degree of reduction or intensification required. The general practice is to adopt the standard wet-collodion method of intensification with copper, silver, and iodine and reduction, if necessary, with weak cyanide. Blacken with sodium sulphide.

Retouching

If dot etching is to be employed, the plates require a gelatine substratum, and after final blackening and washing the plate is drained and coated two or three times with Freundorfer retouching solution. After thorough drying, the plate is rinsed, hardened with a 10 per cent solution of formaldehyde, and dried without further washing. The plate is moistened with a 30 per cent glycerine–water solution, and etched in the usual manner with the following—

A.	Iodine	.	.	.	. 3 oz	100 g
	Potassium iodide	.	.	. 3 oz or	100 g
	Water	.	.	. 30 oz	1 litre
B.	Potassium cyanide	.	. 6 oz	200 g
	Water	.	.	. 30 oz or	1 litre

For use mix two parts (A) and five parts (B)

It is important to use these solutions exactly as stated, otherwise difficulties will arise. If too much iodine is used the plates become stained, and with too much cyanide the dots may lose density. The mixed solution will only last for about 24 hours under normal working conditions. It will be found advisable to use a small piece of cotton wool, attached, by twisting, to the end of a suitable stick in preference to brushes, which are likely to be damaged by the strong solution.

The normal methods of "staging" can also be employed, and if a dish is used the reducing solution should be diluted with five times the amount of water.

"Nonsola" Continuous-tone Emulsion

This emulsion is specially suited for continuous-tone negatives or positives. The plates are prepared with the coating solutions as previously described, but the sensitizer for the red coating should not exceed 5 c.c. for each 100 c.c. of coating. Special care must be given regarding thorough shaking of the emulsion prior to coating, for if any of the silver bromide is left as a precipitate, full density will not be obtainable. Careful rocking of the plates is necessary to avoid markings.

Trial exposures can be based on plates having a speed of 45 H. and D., and a satisfactory multiplying factor for colour filters will be 4 to 6. Over-exposure will result in a red or brown colour image, and the negative will have excessive contrast.

Development should be continued for at least two minutes at 65°F., using one of the following—

HARD DEVELOPER

Nonsola concentrated developer . 1 oz } or {	20 c.c.	
Water . . . . . 20 oz } or {	400 c.c.	

MEDIUM DEVELOPER

Nonsola concentrated developer . ½ oz } or {	10 c.c.	
Water . . . . . 20 oz } or {	400 c.c.	

Nonsola concentrated developer . ½ oz ⎫ ⎧ 10 c.c.
Water . . . . 20 oz ⎬ or ⎨ 400 c.c.
0·880 ammonia 40–80 minims ⎭ ⎩ 2–4 c.c.

Extra soft results can be obtained by adding more ammonia.

Any of the methods for reducing or intensifying dry plates can be employed for Nonsola emulsion.

Retouching

Density will increase when the emulsion is dry, and it may be advisable to apply a hard negative varnish. If this is standard practice, polished plates can be used.

If a similar type of surface to a dry plate is desired, a warm 10 per cent solution of gelatine is flowed over the surface after a final washing in warm water. Plates to be so treated must have a gelatine substratum.

The Nonsola emulsion can also be treated with Freundorfer retouching solution, as previously described, if it is desired to employ local chemical reduction, using a very dilute cyanide and iodine solution.

General

For critical work it is advisable to apply a backing immediately before exposure. A suitable solution can be prepared with gum arabic, lamp-black and glycerine.

To facilitate coating the plates with emulsion an orange safelight can be used, provided the necessary green or ruby safelight is used when applying the coating solution.

In view of the stencil-like dot formation the application of dye to a half-tone negative is not usefully effective, except to a very limited extent, but an equivalent result can be obtained by making a fully exposed negative or positive and "staging."

SECTION 7. PROJECTION

Projection methods are covering a much wider field recently, not only in the production of enlarged screen negatives as previously described, but by direct reproduction from the several types of miniature colour transparencies now perfected, and projection direct to the metal plate, which is described on page 210.

In some cases special apparatus has been installed for the production of enlarged films up to, say, 60 in. × 40 in. Preferably, the apparatus is in the form of a dark-room camera. The lens must adequately cover the size of negative concerned, coupled with the degree of enlargement, and in view of the critical nature of the work the selection should be as generous as possible. The mounting for the lens is attached to the dark-room wall, and can include bellows, together with an adjustment for fine focusing. The transparency holder is adjustably mounted on floor rails, and if the lens is not adjustable the control for the transparency holder should be extended into the dark-room. The easel can be provided with an extension to the rear to support a white roller blind or similar reflecting surface. A "four-point" arc lamp unit is ideal for this purpose, and perfectly even illumination is obtainable, or the lamps can be arranged to provide slightly extra illumination at the corners when the optical equipment is being operated at the upper limits of the covering capacity. The lamps may be mounted on tripods or hung from swinging lamp arms fixed to the wall.

The plate holder in the dark-room will be constructed according to probable requirements; if film only is to be used, a specially constructed vacuum frame can be employed. This will be of the face-down type, arranged with a positive lock for the vertical position, and mounted on floor rails with suitable mechanism for focusing. If plates are to be used, it will be necessary to have a plate-holding frame, which may vary extensively in its design, according to available expenditure, and may also include screen gear, so that the projection apparatus can be used as a normal camera. Provision should be made for holding two $\frac{1}{4}$-in. plate-glasses as a support for films.

There are, of course, several possible arrangements of projection apparatus, and the standard camera can itself be used by arranging for the studio to be convertible into a dark-room, and fitting a separate illuminant, consisting of mercury-vapour tubes mounted in a light-tight box attached to a suitable stand, which in turn runs on the camera rails. This unit can be clamped to the back body of the camera and the screen gear used for holding the transparency, or it can be arranged to clamp to the dark-slide, which is left in position, but without shutter or door. This arrangement would be used for the following interesting process.

The sensitive film or plate is positioned in the copy holder or on the copy-board.

The process just mentioned is a method of producing enlarged screen plates from continuous-tone transparencies, and has been developed by Freundorfer in connexion with collodion emulsion. The transparency holder must incorporate a screen gear to enable a fine screen to be positioned between the transparency and lens, and at a distance governed by the normal factors. The projected image is focused to correct size, and trial exposures will indicate the effects of lens aperture, screen distance, and exposure time.

Upon visualizing this process one would imagine that as in effect the screen itself is being enlarged, the result would simply be a negative of the screen, i.e. a series of squares, all more or less the same size, but varying in density according to the light passed by the transparency. Actually, however, an extremely good dot formation can be obtained, and the characteristics of collodion emulsion play a great part in the success which has been evidenced; it will be remembered that a wide degree of intensification is possible, and after final blackening, correction

COLOUR-FILM ENLARGING UNIT, SEEN ATTACHED TO CAMERA

is readily carried out as described on page 135, the dots having a core which enables reduction down to a vanishing pin-point, without loss of density.

The technique of this process is, however, not widely known at present, and the general practice is to project from a screen negative. If a poster of, say, 40 in. × 30 in. is required, having a ruling of between 35 and 40 lines per inch, and a 150-line screen is available, this would mean an enlargement of four diameters, and the negative would therefore be made 10 in. × $7\frac{1}{2}$ in.

There are various types of film and film paper which will be found quite satisfactory, and upon which the manufacturers will advise. A commonly used paper has a translucent base, the shrinkage of which is fairly constant, and if proper precautions are taken regarding standard manipulation during the development, fixing, washing, and drying (particularly the last) quite satisfactory register can be obtained for colour work. "Grainless" miniature colour transparencies such as Kodachrome and Agfacolor are likely to be used to a considerable extent as originals, although doubtless there will be a still greater application of the larger colour transparencies which are becoming available in this form such as Ektachrome or Anscocolour.

Small films can be enlarged better by the addition of a "Colour Transparency Projection Unit" to the standard camera unit. This apparatus permits considerable enlargement with sharpness and registration, resulting from the apochromatic enlarging lenses and gelatine colour filters used. The unit is precision built.

If much of this work is contemplated it is advisable to obtain a special fitting which can be rigidly attached direct to the camera front. This comprises a lens panel and transparency housing, one of which is adjustable for focusing, and possibly an independent lamp house with suitable diffuser. Although normal tri-colour filters can be used, it is advisable to obtain special filters supplied by the film manufacturers, and these are preferably mounted between the transparency and light source, and must be easily interchangeable without risk of affecting the camera setting.

The colour-separated negatives can be retouched and proceeded with in the normal manner for indirect reproduction. A standard enlarger, if of rigid construction, can be used for this purpose, but it is very unusual to find one available in a photo-litho department.

In view of the rapidly advancing technique following the experience of users, it is advised that suppliers of colour film be requested to furnish details of the latest practice and facilities recommended for reproduction purposes.

CHAPTER VIII

DUPLICATE NEGATIVES

THERE are many occasions when a negative is required consisting of several repeats of the same subject. If the quantity of such work does not justify the installation of special equipment some method must be devised as a compromise which will produce the required results: this can only be done within certain narrow limits, however. For single-colour work a number of wet collodion or strip-film negatives could be made and stripped on to one glass; but if, as frequently occurs with newly installed photo-litho departments, the originals are already drawn on stones or plates, a number of impressions may be pulled on dull enamel paper and carefully positioned on a sheet of zinc. A negative is taken of this group, and impressions of the second colour are "patched-up" over the first set and a second negative made. The second set is removed and successive ink impressions similarly patched-up and photographed. The register marks of the second and following sets will have to be punched or cut as in common litho practice for sighting the underlying register marks.

If the subject is a line sketch or similar original, a negative is first made, say twice the size of the final requirements. Contact bromide prints can be made from this and positioned on a lay-out which is drawn to the same scale of enlargement as the prints. A correct size negative from this group should retain all the finest detail. The same method may be applied to the production of half-tone multi-negatives.

Various methods such as the above cannot be employed for work requiring a great number of repeats or for high-class precision work: special "Step and Repeat" machines are essential. These machines are capable of a much greater variety of work than is generally realized. Not only can they be used for straight multi-negatives for stamps, labels, cheque backgrounds, etc., but for interlocking designs for book covers, textiles, etc., and elaborate scroll and rosette designs can be stepped up and finally combined in the form of bromide prints to make enlarged originals, which when re-photographed and printed by offset have every appearance of the most expensive copper-plate engraving.

The Hunter-Penrose Step and Repeat Projector is designed to cover a wide application and built to ensure absolute accuracy. The essentials of such a machine are, briefly, an enlarging and reducing projecting apparatus with a rotatable carrier for the unit negative or positive, and a glass-holding frame which can be mechanically adjusted to bring any point of the glass opposite the projector lens. The accuracy demanded of such apparatus requires the whole machine to be of extremely rigid and strong construction with every movement mechanically perfect and with no possiblity of movement or vibration between the projecting and plate-holding parts of the machine. The Hunter-Penrose machine is built on a heavy and absolutely rigid iron base. The unit carrier with adapters for various size units up to 10 in. × 12 in. is rotatable to any degree for building rosette designs or turning the image to any required angle. A special lighting unit consisting of six mercury vapour tubes (non-tilting type) is housed in a light-tight box and arranged to give perfectly even illumination over the maximum size unit. The plate-holding frame is operated from the side of the machine by two hand cranks, one for horizontal and one for vertical movement. Each complete rotation of a crank moves the plate carrier $\frac{1}{10}$ of an inch. The cranks rotate over large dials divided by 100 positioning holes. The adjustment of the frame can thus be

STEP AND REPEAT PROJECTOR

controlled to $\frac{1}{1000}$ of an inch. In order to eliminate calculation and ensure operation being as speedy as possible a very simple and ingenious device is incorporated in the form of a numbered slip-ring on each dial. After each adjustment of the frame, this slip-ring can be quickly rotated to bring the zero mark opposite the pointer. Scales are also provided for checking the number of complete rotations made and the position of the frame at any time. An unusual feature is the duplication of the focusing controls which enables the machine to be used as a camera by first placing an etched glass in the unit carrier for focusing purposes and then replacing this with the sensitive plate.

Automatic focusing has purposely not been included, for the designers maintain, and we agree, that the advantages of absolute accuracy and the very high quality of work to which such machines owe their justification, coupled with a wide range of enlargement and reduction with various lens apertures, would have to be sacrificed to some degree if automatic focusing were included.

The operation of the machine is extremely simple: take for example a negative consisting of several hundred duplicate images of a small label. The original is photographed with either the studio camera or the step and repeat machine. This negative may be several times larger than the final unit images. After masking out it is placed in the unit carrier and the projected image focused on the screen to, say, twice the required size. It is then aligned by rotation of the carrier, this operation being carried out from the front of the machine. All white lights are now switched off and a dry plate or wet collodion plate not exceeding 12 in. × 10 in. positioned in the holder. A series of exposures are made by an electrically operated shutter, which exposes according to the operator's setting of a light-integrating meter. A photo-electric cell incorporated records a quantity of light which can be repeated with great accuracy. In this way, any variation in light output from the tubes in the lamphouse can be automatically compensated. A system of switches permits independent control of the shutter, when required, for focusing and similar purposes.

At the end of each row the frame and plate are raised ready for the following row. After developing and fixing, the enlarged multi-positive thus obtained is masked and placed in the unit carrier ready for projection. This time the projected image must be focused to the correct size. The methods instructed for focusing to size and for alignment enable this to be done with absolute accuracy and without numerous photographic tests. The final plate, which can be of any size up to 30 in. × 40 in., is placed in the holder and a series of exposures made in the same manner as when making the multi-positive. Each exposure will of course project a block of several images.

When working with wet collodion, the length of time for which the plate can be left in the machine is naturally limited, but 20–30 exposures and adjustments can easily be made even under poor conditions before the plate becomes too dry. Consequently, working with a multi-positive of 30 repeats, a final negative made with say 20 exposures will consist of 600 repeats.

If the number of desired repeats runs into thousands and wet collodion is to be used throughout it is only a matter of building up through an additional multi-positive and multi-negative.

Duplicate negatives by contact with a positive can also be produced on certain types of step and repeat printing-down machines, such as are produced by Messrs. Hunter-Penrose, Ltd. and Pictorial Machinery, Ltd. The machines need to be of such a pattern and performance that contact between various thicknesses of glass negatives can be carefully controlled so that no damage results from the contact made. Negatives or positives so used should have only the minimum amount of surface opaquing, and even that must be carefully applied.

CHAPTER IX

RETOUCHING

THE question as to why retouching and colour correction is necessary apart from alterations or faulty originals involves matters of ink value and transparency, paper quality, methods of printing, etc. Very close approximation to the original can be obtained so far as pure photography is concerned, but the necessary interposition of the half-tone screen, and methods of obtaining high-light negatives, cause a deviation from continued straight-line or facsimile reproduction. These factors and other individual limitations need not be dwelt on here—retouching *is* necessary in present-day colour work, and the notes which follow are concerned with the methods to be employed.

A separate room should be allocated to this work, with water supply for washing negatives after chemical retouching, etc., and some form of heating such as an electric hot-air fan for ensuring absolute dryness of films which are to be worked with pencils, scrapers, etc. The arrangement of the table or bench must allow for a good illumination of the original which should always be available for reference when working on the negatives.

The various materials used are selected according to preference following the retoucher's individual experience, together with the work undertaken. Mention is made in the following instructions of all the apparatus and materials likely to be employed.

The use of a shining-up table is not recommended if much work has to be done, for the retoucher would be in a very strained position and this would lead to irregular or inferior work.

Special retouching desks can be purchased which consist essentially of a sloping opal or ground-glass frame with side pieces or curtains to cut off side-light. Similar protection against overhead light is also advised. A flat white surface such as a sheet of blotting paper at the back of the desk gives the necessary illumination by reflected light from a window or a lamp.

Fluorescent tube lighting or reflected daylight is popular. Other forms of illumination usually create heat to the detriment of the negative and its supporting diffused glass. Masking blinds are sometimes preferred to cut off the extraneous light which surrounds the negative and can lead the retoucher to misjudge the tone values of the negative or positive.

Wet collodion negatives do not lend themselves to extensive retouching, and work other than spotting is rarely attempted. As these are usually made from retouched monochrome originals or positives, further hand work should not be required. If, however, this is really necessary the reduction or "opening" will have to be done chemically while in the hands of the operator, that is, by means of a weak potassium cyanide solution following the iodine treatment. The artist can strengthen or increase the density only to a limited extent. The negative is invariably flowed over with a gum solution before leaving the operator's hands, and this solution could be slightly thicker than normal: when absolutely dry it may be "matted" by gently rubbing over with a little finest washed emery powder, using two or three thicknesses of tissue paper as a pad. It will then take soft pencil work quite well, but care must be taken not to scratch the film. Alternatively, matt varnish is applied either on the back of the glass or on the film which has been first protected with a coating of hard negative varnish. When applying any varnish the negative must be thoroughly dry and slightly warm and rocked during draining as when coating with collodion. The varnish must be allowed ample time to harden before attempting to work on it.

The effect of this work is at best rather indefinite, except perhaps in the near high-lights, and it will probably be found worth while to use a grained shading medium after first coating the negative with a protective varnish. A suitable film can be found in practically every litho artists' department. It is advisable to dust the ink impression with bronze powder which not only builds up the density but prevents the ink offsetting to the metal when printing down. If any painting out with opaque is necessary this is preferably completed before using the shading medium. Special precautions must be taken when using opaque to ensure that no thick portions or lumps are allowed to form, for these would seriously affect the perfect contact which is so important when printing to metal. To examine a negative for such faults it is held in a horizontal position slightly below the level of the eye, when any raised portions will become immediately apparent. These must be scraped down.

Margins of the negative can be either painted out or masked with tin-foil. The advantages of tin-foil warrant a much greater use than is generally found in the average shop. It is extremely thin and gives an absolutely opaque ground without any fear of loss of contact. In fact it can be used on a screen negative in place of lining out with a ruling pen and paint. If the materials are always to hand it will be found that negatives can be masked out in a much shorter time than by other methods. A few words of caution as to its use are necessary. The foil is supplied in 1-lb rolls. These should be carefully unrolled and stored flat in, say, an old negative box. A few sheets at a time are laid on a piece of glass and with a sharp knife and a steel straight-edge cut into strips of varying width to suit the class of work. A little practice will be necessary before obtaining perfectly straight cuts without creasing and wrinkling. The supply of strips should also be kept in a box close to the retouching desk or shining-up table. To attach the foil to the negative, thin rubber solution or gum can be used as an adhesive. If gum is used the foil is placed on a sheet of clean paper and held down at each end in turn while a few touches of gum are spread by the side of the hand to form a light smear rather than a film. If too much is applied a great deal of it will not dry owing to the sealing effect of the foil, and when the negative is brought into pressure contact with the plate the gum will be squeezed out and damage, or more probably ruin, the plate coating. A double thickness of foil cannot of course be avoided at corners and where strips overlap, but this will not cause any trouble if the above specially thin foil is used.

The most satisfactory method of reducing or etching dry-plate screen negatives (increasing the printing value) is by the use of Farmer's reducer consisting of weak hypo solution and ferri-cyanide solution, or hypo and iodine, the control being assisted by the use of glycerine in the separate or mixed solutions. A common method of applying the above for local work consisted of soaking the film in a hypo solution and then applying a 10 per cent solution of ferricyanide or weak iodine where necessary, using a brush or cotton-wool.

The above procedure has been very carefully elaborated and standardized by Kodak Ltd., whose book dealing very thoroughly with the subject should be studied. They suggest the use of a strong solution of hypo (approximately 50 per cent) with equal parts of glycerine, the mixture being well rubbed into the film. The required reduction is effected by applying with brush or cotton-wool a 30 per cent solution of potassium ferricyanide to which has also been added an equal proportion of glycerine. When reduction has reached the required stage, further action is prevented by rubbing over again with the hypo and glycerine. The whole plate can be worked over and corrected to any degree by using the two solutions alternately. For fine detail work the surface of the film is wiped free of the hypo solution before applying ferricyanide, while for vignettes and softer results a liberal coating of hypo is left on the film. It is recommended that negatives which are to receive the above treatment should be fixed in a hypo solution to which has been added potassium iodide in the proportion of one part to each 200 parts of solution. The use of Kodak "Peridak Staging Paint" will be found very useful for painting in isolated portions of the film such as lettering and ruled lines which do not require reducing while treating the surrounding portions. The paint can also be used for "staging," that is painting out all portions not to be reduced, immersing in a weak hypo-ferricyanide solution, drying, again painting out and reducing; the operation being repeated until the desired effect is obtained. The Peridak staging paint can finally be removed with a solvent consisting of amyl acetate one part, alcohol two parts.

Several alternative preparations may be used for staging purposes, such as amber varnish, or some of the coloured brushing cellulose lacquers. Turpentine or amyl acetate and alcohol or paraffin are used as solvents.

Iodine and cyanide solutions as used for wet collodion may also be employed in place of ferricyanide and hypo, and in some quarters are preferred, as the mixed solution is more stable. The solution must be well diluted to afford the desired control for any particular class of work, and as the artist is probably on unfamiliar ground when handling chemicals, he must be warned of the highly poisonous nature of cyanide.

It has been found that with certain plates and films a fairly strong residual image is left after reduction with ferricyanide. This can be removed by immersion in a 5 or 10 per cent solution of potassium cyanide, followed by washing.

Attention is again drawn to the note that negatives to be treated as above should not be intensified: the application of plain hypo on an intensified plate has itself a reducing action, bringing the image back to its original condition.

After all local or staging reduction is completed the negative is thoroughly washed and can then be intensified where necessary by local application of a mercury bichloride bleacher followed by prolonged washing and final blackening in weak ammonia. A limited degree of intensification can be obtained with a single-solution intensifier—

1. Mercuric chloride 1 part, water 30 parts.
2. Potassium iodide 3 parts, water 10 parts.
3. Sodium acetate $2\frac{1}{2}$ parts; hypo $1\frac{1}{2}$ parts; water 20 parts. Add No. 2 to No. 1 until the precipitate first formed dissolves, then add No. 3.

(This should be preceded by immersion in 1 per cent acetic acid to minimize risk of stains.)

In practice, however, the majority of artists will prefer to increase density by other means such as dyeing and pencilling. Hunter-Penrose Photo Dye or good quality water-soluble red dye can be used by applying to a wet film. The surplus solution is wiped away with wet cotton-wool immediately after application; this leaves a stain on the film and graded or vignette effects can thus be obtained very readily. Of course one cannot expect to convert a near shadow into a comparatively light tone by this method, but all tones can be considerably modified without seriously impairing the printing quality of the negative. An air-brush can also be used for the same purpose.

Pencilling will be found the most satisfactory method of dealing with small detail work. For this purpose the film must be absolutely dry and a tooth formed on the gelatine by rubbing over with hard medium rough paper. This must be of good quality and free from particles of grit, etc., which would scratch the film. With some films it is difficult to get a tooth in this manner, in which case a little finest washed emery powder rubbed over the surface with the palm of the hand and a sheet of smooth thin paper will give the desired result. The matt surface thus produced will readily take pencil work as long as the film is kept thoroughly dry. In this connexion the artist must be cautioned against working in such a position that his breath condenses on the negative. An attempt should be made to apply the right pencil pressure with a suitable pencil on the first strokes rather than repeatedly working over the same spot. Practice is naturally essential, as in all such operations, and the artist should obtain several discarded negatives, apply work in the several ways suggested and get them printed to metal in the normal manner in order to take careful note of the effect his work has on the final print for future guidance. The visual and the printing values of retouched negatives are by no means always the same. Further, a negative requiring a generally longer printing exposure than normal will require more vigorous retouching to take effect.

"Retouching medium" (a special resin varnish) can also be used to produce a pencilling surface. This must be applied to the film very thinly, using a piece of soft muslin over the finger and rubbing with a circular motion over the whole surface. The varnish must be allowed to harden thoroughly.

The methods suggested for wet plate may be employed, and if desired the matt varnish can be coated on the film side, no protective varnish being necessary. The objection to using any type of varnish on the film side is that further reduction which may be found advisable becomes extremely difficult.

The query may be raised about the efficacy of pencilling a screen negative. Obviously the best printing negative is of wet collodion characteristics and corrected in both directions by an increase or decrease of the actual size of the dots. The direct dry-plate screen negative, however, has a slight veil or fringe surrounding each opaque dot. While this is partly eliminated during chemical reduction, it may be used, together with the comparative thickness of the film, to enable pencil work to be usefully employed. Only the centre of each clear negative dot is of maximum transparency and when printing to metal the coating immediately under this point of maximum transparency is rendered insoluble first. As the exposure continues and sufficient light action occurs below the veiled portions so the insoluble dot increases progressively. Now, where the film has been dyed or pencilled the effective exposure is reduced, and only the points of maximum transparency or the immediately adjacent film—according to the strength of retouching—pass sufficient light during the standard exposure period to form a firm printing dot. Under such conditions of course the printing exposure times become critical as compared with the wide margin which is permissible with a wet collodion negative, or a dry plate with similar characteristics.

For reducing density while the film is dry some abrasive paste specially manufactured for the purpose can be used, or methylated spirit and finest pumice or emery powder. Either of these can be rubbed over the film, using hard stumps or wood sticks shaped to a blunt point. An artist's scraper, razor blade, or even tools made out of hack-saw blades or similar metal and shaped to suit requirements can be used to reduce a negative to a great extent without necessarily destroying the characteristics of the screen image. Considerable practice must be given to the use of tools in this way. The main point to watch is that the tools are kept razor sharp at all times and a fine oil-stone must be kept to hand for constant use. If the film is kept absolutely dry and the blade drawn across with a very light touch, fine surface shavings can be removed without scratching the film. Difficulty will be experienced if the film has been hardened with alum or formaline. Such treatment should not therefore be given unnecessarily.

When reducing a screen negative to obtain a solid print there is no necessity to continue the chemical or abrasive action to the point where the dense dots entirely disappear: they should only be reduced to a degree which is known to produce a solid. If this precaution is not taken false *visual* values will be created, for there will be several tones at the bottom end of the scale which appear to have differing values yet will all produce solids. The artist must give this point careful attention and ascertain the minimum size of opaque dot which will retain the deepest shadow detail under existing conditions of exposure and plate coating.

Continuous-tone negatives and positives can be reduced by the chemical means described or rubbed down with abrasive paste (sometimes metal polish) or scraped. They can be strengthened by pencilling, etc., after either matting or preparing with retouching medium. Air-brush and dyes can also be used.

Dry-plate screen positives are treated chemically for lightening tones as described for reducing dry-plate screen negatives, and solids are painted in with opaque.

Films are of course treated in the same manner as dry plates, with the exception of the use of matt varnish which is too difficult to coat satisfactorily and consistently on film. Most manufacturers can now supply film with a special matt surface for retouching.

When working an indirect process the artist should have a clear and definite idea as to the work which will be done at each stage according to the methods he adopts. For example, take a continuous-tone negative, screen positive and contact final negative: strengthening of printing tones may be accomplished by chemical or abrasive reduction of the first negative; weakening of tones by chemical reduction on the screen positive; solids painted in on the positive, and high-lights painted in on the final negative, this also being masked with tin-foil.

If one's work and the final results are carefully and continually noted from the start it will result in a great saving of the time which is so often wasted in "playing" minute detail which is better left entirely alone. An experienced artist turns out better and quicker work not necessarily because of his better sense of colour values but principally on account of his ability to distinguish between essential corrections and ineffectual detail.

It is again strongly recommended that artists commencing this work obtain as much practice as possible on the modification of black and white reproductions. Only by this experience will they grasp the main essentials of the work they have to do, and the amount of negative alteration which is necessary to obtain a desired result. It is, of course, of utmost importance that standardized printing-down methods be rigidly adhered to, otherwise the early experience of artists would just be a series of apparent contradictions.

With regard to corrections for colour there is little definite instruction which can be given and artists will have to rely on their assumed previous chromo-litho experience, bearing in mind the important modification regarding number of printings. Particular care must be given when determining the values required for, say, four printings where the artist has been used to working in seven or eight. Success will depend on the ability to adapt oneself to the new conditions and possibilities, and the pains taken in observing and mentally tabulating the results of corrections.

If the photography and printing on metal are of the high standard to which it is hoped these directions will contribute, little correction will probably be found necessary with certain types of subject such as clean water-colours, particularly if these are wisely designed with a view to ease of reproduction. The following notes regarding a few colours and their common trichromatic reproduction without hand work will prove of assistance.

Assuming correct photography and a printing order of yellow, red and blue, with reasonably transparent inks, colours predominating in yellow and red reproduce with the nearest approach to the original; thus yellow, flesh, orange, warm browns and reds should not necessitate retouching on any of the negatives, except, perhaps, a slight strengthening of the reds to maintain the brightness of the reproduction.

Light brown tends to reproduce with too much red.

Pink tends to reproduce with too much yellow.

Cold reds and purples tend to reproduce with too much yellow and insufficient blue.

Light blues tend to reproduce with too much red.

Green blues tend to reproduce with too much red and insufficient blue.

Warm blues tend to reproduce with too much yellow and insufficient blue.

Neutral greys tend to reproduce with too much red.

The above are based on a wide variety of originals and pigments, and must therefore be taken as a general indication of what may be expected with average conditions.

It will be remembered that the "black negative" is made to give a monochromatic rendering of the coloured sketch. Every colour has a value which can be rendered in terms of black and white, and consequently if the negative were printed without hand correction it would give a tint wherever colour existed on the sketch. This of course is not desired, for the colours are already supplied in their respective printings, and the presence of the black would only degrade them. The object of the black printing is to assist in the "form" or "drawing" and give a depth to the reproduction which would otherwise be lacking. The black printer negative can be relied upon also to give a duality to brown tints by blending with the yellow and red, more so than can the blue negative. It was advised that the negative be made rather more dense and contrasty than standard: this helps considerably towards the effect aimed at, but hand work will be essential—mostly in reduction of the printing value, and "opaquing" for clean primary and secondary colours.

Tint negatives and positives are retouched with main regard to the light tones, painting out the high-lights and those portions where even a tint is likely to degrade an opposing colour. Experience will show that quite broad and vigorous retouching only is required here.

The general nature of the complete design, the conditions under which it will be printed and materials to be used must be taken into consideration when retouching.

Consider, as an example, a four-colour poster on which a large panel of solid red appears; the same red printing has to serve for all purposes and probably the paper to be used will be of comparatively poor quality. To obtain the necessary solid and at the same time avoid "fluffing," a full charge of fairly soft ink will be used. This would normally ruin the tones of the pictorial part of the design, particularly if it is in a fairly fine screen; the artist must anticipate this difficulty and ensure that a light image is produced, particularly in the middle and three-quarter tones. This is of course a compromise, but it is one of several which have to be effected very frequently in practice.

Before leaving the subject of retouching, it is stressed that the aim should be to reduce to a minimum the amount of artist's work on the negative. This can only be effected successfully by the closest co-operation of every department, commencing wherever possible with the design of the sketch. This procedure is in fact being given the most careful investigation in some establishments, particularly, for instance, where specialized work such as box tops and coloured labels in, say, four colours is being undertaken, and every effort is made towards standardization. A definite selection of inks is decided upon and adhered to, with the exception of perhaps extra printings for backgrounds.

Research and experiment in colour filtering and colour masking in negative making, combined with the manufacture of more suitable inks, are all leading to the ultimate end where only a minimum of hand retouching will be necessary to effect a desired result.

Such reproduction tendencies as excessive red in the greens are anticipated and taken care of in the designing department by modifying the greens in the sketch, i.e. making them colder than will finally be required. Carefully standardized exposures in the production of negatives and positives, using graded strips for checking purposes, are followed by simple outlining, highlighting, and any work necessitated by lettering, etc. Humidity control in printing-down and pressrooms, careful adjustment of machines and other obvious precautions, have all to be given attention—it will be realized that the fewer the printings the more critical must be the control of methods and conditions throughout.

CHAPTER X

PLATE PREPARATION

SECTION 1. THE LITHOGRAPHIC PLATE

THE initial preparation of lithographic plates has a decided bearing on the eventual success of a photo-litho reproduction, and while a line of demarcation must be made at some stage of these instructions a few remarks are considered advisable in view of the number of inferior results observed and traced to trouble occurring before the plate reaches the printing-down department.

The majority of houses obtain their new plates ready grained from the suppliers, whose advice can be taken regarding the texture of grain most suitable for the general class of work undertaken.

The caution which we wish to emphasize with particular stress and which applies at all times during the lithographic life of the plate is directed against what is admittedly one of the most persistent and frequent sources of trouble—oxidization.

It may occur immediately after graining, during storing, while in the hands of the metal printer or artist, or on the press. In its milder form it may not be apparent on the plate but when printing commences or has been in progress for a short period a "scum" or patchy "rotting" occurs which frequently renders the plate useless, and at the best requires very skilled attention and much expenditure of time to eradicate without damaging the printing image.

Experienced houses should need no reminder of the precautions which should be taken by their staff, but the trouble is so liable to arise following rather obscure causes that continual attention is always necessary.

The preparation and use of a lithographic plate is essentially associated with water at practically every stage. This in itself is quite harmless: it is during the subsequent drying that the oxidization occurs. The drying must always be completed as quickly as possible with due regard against over-heating. The plate must never be left in a damp state or in a damp atmosphere. The latter applies in particular to storing at any stage. The prevalent but misinformed belief that a gummed plate is immune to oxidization causes much heated dispute as to the source of scum; a plate which has been gummed over and then left for a lengthy period in a semi-dry state is certainly liable to future scumming, as also a gummed plate stored in a damp corner of the shop, or subjected to periodical damp draughts (on the machine during non-working hours, for instance). To enumerate all the possible conditions under which oxidization may occur would provide a lengthy and apparently trifling list: suffice it again to stress to every department, from graining to press room, the importance of ensuring as far as possible that the plate is either definitely wet or thoroughly dry, the intermediate state being reduced to a minimum period.

The majority of departments will do their own graining and this operation should be given much greater consideration and study than is frequently the case. The quality and texture of the grain *is* important, and each plate should be given a very thorough examination with a powerful magnifying glass or binocular microscope to check the evenness and quality of grain throughout, particularly following any variation of procedure.

The ever-present opposing requirements regarding fine or coarse grain as demanded by the plate preparation departments and machine room must be a matter for consideration. A compromise has mostly to be effected but not necessarily a compromise between such widely separated extremes as is generally supposed. The metal printer claims that he cannot make a clear well-defined print on a coarse grain—the machine minder says he cannot keep the work or maintain correct damping with a fine grain. Each is probably right according to his own experience. Modifications can be made in the metal printing department when necessary to enable a reasonably good print to be made on a coarse grain but that print despite all the skill and experience available is certainly not the best possible. For best results in that department one is certainly justified in demanding a medium or fine grain.

The machine minder who persistently demands a coarser grain has quite good reasons for this also, but they are frequently reasons based—unwittingly, perhaps—on the consequences of overcoming trouble which is remediable in other directions more closely associated with the root of the difficulty. For instance, the statement that the work or grain quickly wears off when using a medium texture: assuming a plate correctly prepared at the outset the machine may be adjusted for too much pressure, this following the use of a blanket in a poor condition, and this in turn perhaps following the use of an inferior blanket-wash or faulty treatment: the blanket cylinder may not be of the same periphery as the plate cylinder, this causing continual scrubbing; such variation may have been intentional, due to common methods of overcoming paper stretch, this again on account of the use of inferior paper or lack of conditioning: damping or inking rollers may be causing excessive scrubbing; unsuitable inks may lead to a train of remedies which in turn cause effects which apparently indicate the advisability of a coarser grain.

These suggestions could be multiplied, but the above are sufficient to show that the medium grain is not itself the true cause of the cry against it. One does not always expect to find ideal conditions of machines, paper and ink, etc., but when difficulties do arise overseers should carefully trace the trouble to its source and endeavour to eliminate it there rather than tacitly accept the demand for a coarser grain and thereby introduce another partial remedy which in itself is liable to prove a hindrance to good work. Of course there are frequently enforced conditions either extant or pending which justify a modification of standard photo grain for a particular machine or job, and this is certainly a matter for compromise. The quality of the finished work will probably be below standard, but if unsuitable paper or ink or a defective machine is used the best results cannot be expected.

It must be added, however, that much of the trouble could be traced to poor *quality* of grain rather than wrong texture. The close examination of many plates actually in use but causing trouble revealed a surface which appeared comparatively flat with a few scattered holes and scratches, and it is remarkable that any results at all were obtained. The surface should present an even and regular tooth, as sharp and "close" as possible, and without smooth-sided scratches or flat spots. Such a plate with reasonably good printing conditions gives better results when dealing with the class of work under discussion than a coarse grain of inferior quality.

The choice of zinc or aluminium is another question which until recently was exceedingly controversial. The experience and views of authorities in favour of either metal could be quoted, but the prevailing popularity of zinc appears a sufficiently convincing answer to the query. Apart from minor points one of the principal claims for aluminium was that it produced a cleaner and sharper impression, but when the reasons for the claim are fully examined they are found to be closely connected with general manipulation and probably arrived at following certain faulty machine-room practices, the results of which were less evident when using aluminium. With a correctly adjusted machine and with a full understanding of both metals one can get equally good results from both zinc and aluminium.

There are the further questions regarding susceptibility to oxidization, mechanical strength, transferring, alterations, suitability for intaglio etching processes, etc., but when these are thoroughly sifted the balance in favour of zinc justifies its ever-increasing adoption.

SECTION 2. GRAINING

New and ungrained plates should first be scoured with pumice powder and water and then examined to decide the better side. Used plates must have the ink image removed with turpentine or similar solvent, and then the surface thoroughly cleaned with a caustic potash solution and pumice powder, using a plate-cleaning machine as illustrated, or if one of these is not included in the installation the plate must be well scrubbed with a brass wire brush and caustic.

Graining machines are more or less of a standard type consisting of a shallow tray to which can be imparted a horizontal rotary motion with a radius of approximately one inch. There are more elaborate models which have marble sifting and washing devices, mainly operated by hydraulic lift, and relieve the operator of much wasted time. The speed should be variable within certain limits, a maximum of 200 r.p.m. being usually adequate. The plate is either clamped or tacked to a false bottom and then covered with marbles of a size suited to requirements. For average photo-litho work these can be either glass or porcelain of about one inch in diameter, to be used with graining material passed through a 120 sieve (48 continental). Heavier marbles, such as stainless steel, are considered suitable for coarse and deep grain, with resulting longer printing life to the plate. There are several good graining materials available, including pumice powder, ground glass, sand flint, emery, etc., the last-named being particularly suitable. These should be obtained from a reliable supply house to ensure the correct grade or elimination of finer or coarser material than that stipulated. It is not always realized that if unclassified material is obtained and then sifted

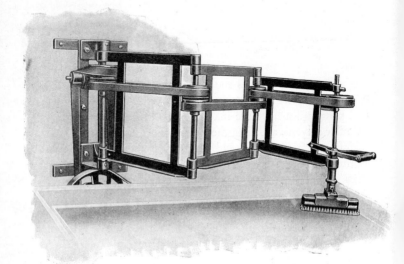

LITHO PLATE-CLEANING MACHINE

through a sieve of known mesh the material will include a large proportion of much finer powder than that required.

Before the machine is set in motion water and graining material are sprinkled evenly over the marbles. A common error is the use of too much of either or both: the plate should only be moistened and only sufficient graining material added to give a good cutting effect without clogging or impeding the free movement of the marbles. One of the principal factors governing successful graining is close attention to the periodic addition of fresh material and water. Experience and careful note of results will be the best guide regarding quantities, but it will be found that frequent application (about every 10 minutes) of small quantities will give much more regular and satisfactory results than larger quantities at greater intervals. The final

LITHO PLATE-GRAINING MACHINE

period should be slightly longer, say 12–14 minutes. The total period of graining will also have to be ascertained by observation, but if a plate is reasonably clean at the outset, half an hour should suffice. This can only be taken as a very rough average, however. Many experienced grainers recommend the use of a slightly coarser material during the last period. While it is difficult to explain a full justification for this practice, it must be conceded that good results are often obtained.

If a finer grain is wanted for subsequent transferring process, etc., a finer material should be used. Pumice powder is best for the very fine grains. When a slightly finer grain than normal is required and the correct material is not immediately available it is possible to use the standard grade and allow longer periods between applications of fresh material, particularly for the last period.

This temporary measure is frequently taken to an absurd excess and instances have been observed where "poster sand" has been used exclusively for all plates. The work naturally suffered.

When the plate has been removed from the machine it must be thoroughly cleaned on both sides; a strong jet of water and a good sponging is essential to remove all trace of graining material. For purposes other than photo-litho the plate should be immersed in an acid bath consisting of 1 part of pure nitric acid and 2 parts of alum to 100 parts of water: a short wash followed by an application of 2 per cent glacial acetic acid gives a whiter appearance to the metal. Finally the plate is thoroughly washed and *dried quickly* in some form of drying rack. If the plate is to be used for photo-litho the acid treatment may be omitted as this is given immediately before coating with the light-sensitive solution. Excessive and unnecessary application of acid has a harmful effect on the sharp and crisp character of the grain.

A procedure which is likely to gain favour is the gumming of plates immediately after graining and before drying. The gum is washed off just before coating with albumen for the printing-down process. Some processes of treating the grained surface, by flowing over chemical solutions to reduce oxidization considerably, have been patented.

After considerable use some of the marbles will acquire "flats" or become cube shaped; these should be discarded as they are likely to cause scratches. Scratches are also caused by careless removal of the plate from the machine. If the marbles cannot be moved to one side of the machine it is a good plan to release the clamps or withdraw the tacks, then allow the machine to rotate slowly while removing the plate. The graining box should be frequently washed out to remove the mud which accumulates.

Latest pattern machines provide for the marbles to leave the graining area under movement, before the plate is lifted from the tray. In this way, marble scratching is reduced to a minimum.

CHAPTER XI

METAL PRINTING

SECTION 1. PREPARATION OF THE PLATE AND EXPOSURE

THE printing of negatives on to metal plates is not in itself a very difficult operation and when seen for the first time by one unacquainted with these processes the reproduction of a good original by means of a well-made negative and efficient clean-cut methods throughout to the completion of the machine plate certainly does appear a matter of extreme simplicity. Much more skill and experience, however, is required at this stage than is generally appreciated; originals are good, bad and indifferent, some may be retouched to approach the imposed standard, others must not be interfered with; the studio may have experienced some incompletely solved difficulty and the retoucher have had to scamp his work owing to rush jobs, so that the metal printer has often to start his own work with a far-from-standard negative quite apart from difficulties of intricate layouts and double printing, etc.

The reader must not infer that the process is a succession of difficulties. Far from it, but instances naturally occur in general work where a previous knowledge of possible difficulties, their cause and the best way of overcoming them, will prevent, we hope, a vast amount of worry and wasted time.

The plate should be examined carefully before use as it is by no means impossible that there should be a fault of some description due to careless handling, or a small chip or flake appear after graining a new plate. If one is unlucky such a fault is sure to fall in an important part of the plate. Serious oxidization due to storing in a damp place will be obvious in the form of stains on the surface, while oxidization of a lesser degree may not make itself apparent until later on, perhaps not until the plate has been running on the machine for a period. The grain must be examined for regularity and texture, and the printer should make himself familiar with all the varying grains which are likely to pass through his hands. In trade houses, particularly, a man has to print on several grain textures during a day's work and he must have a definite knowledge of the necessary modifications for each.

During the following general instructions it will be assumed that zinc plates are used with the recognized medium or fine medium grain most suited to photo-litho.

The general illumination of the metal-printing department need not be reduced to the extent commonly supposed necessary. Strong daylight is of course harmful and the windows should be of amber glass or covered with canary fabric. Ordinary lamps if not of too high a wattage are quite permissible for average manipulations. If the coated plates are likely to be exposed to the general room lighting for lengthy periods, then amber or yellow tinted bulbs should be used.

The metal is first washed and flowed over with pure nitric acid 1 part, alum 2 parts, water 100 parts, then rinsed and similarly treated with glacial acetic acid 2 parts, water 100 parts. A final thorough washing with a strong jet of water and a sponge free from grit or particles of shell is most important to remove all traces of acid and the slight scum or deposit which may have formed. While either one of the above acid treatments is usually sufficient, it is advised that both be included as a precautionary measure. A 1 per cent solution of hydrochloric acid is also frequently used as an alternative. If the plate was gummed immediately after graining, it is only necessary to wash thoroughly, using a sponge and brush, before coating.

The plate is drained for 15 or 20 seconds and placed in a convenient position for coating; this can be obtained by lifting the grid or false bottom on to the near edge of the sink. The plate should slightly overlap the edge of the grid.

The bichromated albumen solution is flowed from left to right over the plate, which is then tilted from side to side to ensure an even coating. A second application should be made

PEDESTAL TYPE WHIRLER

in exactly the same way. It is not advised that the second coating be flowed from the opposite edge to the first as there is always the possibility of foreign matter being picked up from the grid by the edge of the plate and deposited on the working surface after turning.

For evenly spreading and drying the coating a special whirler is employed consisting of a flat turn-table which can be rotated at varying speeds either by hand or power. A splash guard of some kind must be provided and in the latest models the table can be entirely closed in during operation. Heating apparatus is necessary, the best type consisting of electric elements so arranged on the lid of the whirler or on a separate reflecting mount that the whole surface of the plate is dried evenly and without

ELECTRIC HEATER FOR OPEN TYPE WHIRLER

VIEW OF HEATING ELEMENTS

over-heating. The more completely equipped machines can be used for all operations and are fitted with a swinging-arm water supply for washing and a special swinging mount supporting a glass funnel for coating purposes, but the use of this latter appears to be a matter of personal preference. A few installations still employ whirlers with gas heating below the plate, but these should be considered obsolete, for such an arrangement is a constant source of trouble owing to the additional dust and fumes created, damp heat, and heating of the table top with consequent local over-heating of the plate; this eventually results in difficult development, uneven sensitivity, and possibly "scumming" on the printing machine.

The speed of whirling is subject to the grain of the metal and concentration of the sensitizing solution, but 90 to 110 r.p.m. is a suitable speed for average conditions. (Modern whirlers are arranged to cover a speed range of approximately 40 to 90 r.p.m. on account of the requirements of certain reversal processes.) Once the plate has commenced to dry, it is of the greatest importance that no moisture whatever is allowed to attack the coating. It easily happens through the medium of damp masking paper, straw-boards or negatives, and every care must be taken to prevent this.

The coating solution consists of the following—

Dried egg albumen crystals (or flakes)	.	5 oz		160 c.c.
Ammonium bichromate, extra pure	.	1¼ oz	or	40 g
Liquid ammonia 0·880	. approx.	1 oz		32 c.c.
Distilled water up to .	. . .	80 oz		2560 c.c.

The albumen is soaked overnight in part of the quantity of water to be used, or powdered in a perfectly dry mortar, when it can be dissolved more readily. The bichromate is powdered in a mortar, but some water should be added during this operation to prevent bichromate dust. The two solutions are mixed and

A MODERN LITHOGRAPHIC PLATE-COATING, WHIRLING AND
DRYING MACHINE

water added to make up to the required quantity. The ammonia is added slowly and while stirring, until the colour of the solution ust begins to change from orange to a deep yellow. Finally the solution is filtered through cotton-wool placed in the neck of a funnel.

The quality of egg albumen is extremely critical and stocks should not be obtained from sources other than recognized supply houses who only accept supplies samples of which have been critically tested and proved suitable for photographic purposes. Cheap albumen is very expensive—directly, in that much more of the dried crystal has to be used owing to the large proportion of insoluble matter; and indirectly, owing to the varying and unknown concentration of a filtered solution, although a standard formula has been used, this leading to varying results and possible spoilage of plates.

It is a well-advised practice to test carefully a filtered solution which is working satisfactorily with a Baumé hydrometer graduated in tenths of a degree, and maintain this density (at the same temperature) in future. To carry this still further, the following procedure is advised for making up about 1 Winchester solution. Dissolve 5 oz egg albumen in 70 oz water and filter. Test with hydrometer and add water slowly until density registers 2·2° Baumé at 60°F. (when measuring density, the reading should be taken at the bottom of the surface curve formed by the liquid). The amount of bichromate advised for 80 oz albumen solution at 2·2° Baumé is 1½ oz. If the volume of tested albumen solution varies from this quantity the amount of bichromate should be adjusted in proportion. This may be dissolved in some of the albumen solution, using a pestle and mortar.

If ammonia is omitted the solution is more sensitive to the action of light and also, it is important to note, of other factors, such as over-heating, high humidities, etc. Such a solution must also be used the day of mixing.

A glass measure or jug can be used for flowing the solution over the plate. If bubbles have formed they can be blown to one side of the container while tilting this into the pouring position. If, however, when filtering the solution, a piece of string or tape passed through the neck of the funnel is allowed to rest on the bottom of the container the formation of bubbles will be cut down or entirely prevented.

It is necessary to warn new-comers to the trade against carelessness in handling bichromate either in the powder or liquid form. Fortunately, the majority of us are not so ultra-sensitive to direct or indirect contact with chromic acid or bichromate salts as are the few who must take every precaution when working with, or even near, these chemicals. Once the skin is affected one becomes doubly sensitive, so every care should be taken right from the start that no fine particles are allowed to float in the air nor solutions remain on the hands. Providing that such reasonable precautions are taken the majority of workers need have no compunction in handling bichromate to the extent necessary in the usual photo-litho manipulations.

The frames used for printing on to the metal plates are invariably of the vacuum type, of which there are many different designs. That in most general use consists of a metal framework supporting a rubber blanket with a beaded edge: this frame is normally in the horizontal position, and another overhead frame supporting a sheet of $\frac{1}{4}$-in. plate glass can be lowered and clamped by mechanical means with the glass resting on, and forming an airtight joint with, the rubber bead. Sufficient space is left between the glass and rubber blanket to accommodate the plate and negative. The air between the two frames is exhausted by means of a hand or power-driven pump; thus by atmospheric pressure the negative and plate are pressed into close contact one with the other. Another general type of frame is known as the "face-down." Here the main frame supports the plate glass, and the rubber blanket may be either supported in a second frame or merely secured to one of four clamping bars surrounding the glass frame.

Now to return to the coated plate: this is placed face-up on the bed of the vacuum frame (assuming a face-up frame is being used) and the negative, which has been carefully dusted both back and front, is placed film down on the plate and in the required position relative to the gripper edge and side of the plate. A selection of strawboard strips of various sizes and thicknesses should be available and sufficient of these placed around the negative to prevent the plate being pressed over and indented by the edge of the glass. A useful tip in this connexion, and particularly when using thin plates, is to place a sheet of fairly stout strawboard between the back of the plate and the rubber blanket. This has the effect of stiffening the plate and preventing it being indented in circumstances where the strawboard packing around the negative is not wholly effective. If the negative is to be printed several times on the same plate, all parts not actually being exposed must be protected from dirt or moisture by *absolutely dry* paper. Too much emphasis cannot be given to the importance of having such paper, masking paper and strawboard packing thoroughly dry. Preferably they should be dried by heat immediately before use, as the moisture content of our atmosphere, and particularly in a combined printing-down and developing room where water is continually used, is sufficient to render any paper which is lying around even for short periods very liable to cause damage. Plates have frequently been seen which upon development have shown a heavy scum the exact shape of the packing strawboards used. Then followed violent scrubbing which might or might not entirely eliminate the scum. Of course if such action occurs in the same position as a following print the plate will most probably be useless, for by the time the scum has been cleared away the image proper will be seriously damaged to an extent depending on the relative strength of the image and the scum.

The surface of the glass plate which will be in pressure contact with the back of the negative must receive special care and atten-

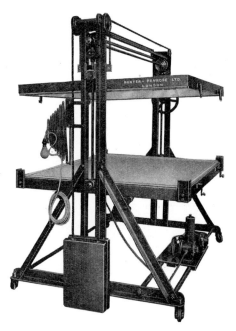

"NEW SERIES" ALL-METAL FACE-UP VACUUM PRINTING FRAME, COUNTERBALANCED MODEL

tion. The smallest piece of hard paper, dried gum, etc., is likely to result in a broken negative; or should the negative be of $\frac{1}{4}$-in. glass there is the possibility of the frame glass being broken. Small particles of grit or gum may easily pass unnoticed by the eye but rarely escape touch. Therefore the hand should always be drawn across the glass surface before lowering the frame into position.

When the pump has created maximum pressure a tap on the connecting tube can be closed, so preventing any leakage of air

ALL-METAL FACE-UP VACUUM PRINTING FRAME
(Printing Position)

into the frame through the pump when the motor is switched off. With the larger sizes of frame, however, it is advisable to keep the motor running continuously while contact is required. In a busy shop and in subdued light a small piece of fluff, etc., on the rubber beading, or other cause of slow leakage, might pass unnoticed, and when the motor is switched off loss of

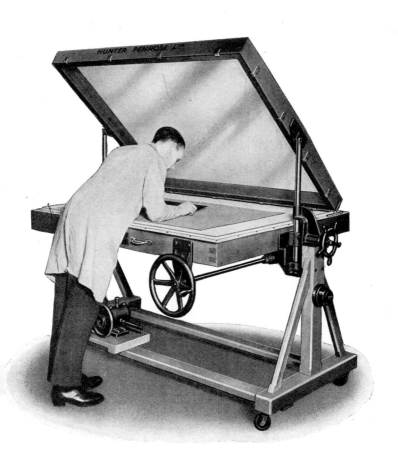

NEW TYPE WOOD MODEL "FACE-UP" VACUUM PRINTING FRAME
Without overhead gear.

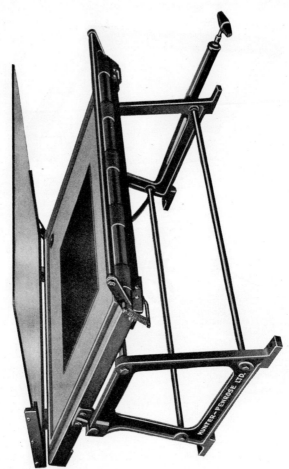

NEW "QUICK LOCK" ALL-METAL VACUUM PRINTING FRAME—BENCH MODEL

contact will follow. In many frames the inclusion of a tap is purposely omitted. Should a serious leakage occur after contact has been obtained this can usually be detected by the sound of

WOOD MODEL FACE-DOWN VACUUM PRINTING FRAME

the pump when motor-driven or by testing the pull of the nozzle against the frame glass. The cause of such a leakage is usually quite apparent, but sometimes the rubber beading itself is the cause of imperfect sealing and consequent loss of contact.

A depressed portion can be located by smearing a thin paste of colour powder, glycerine, and water, on the beading, lowering the glass frame into position without clamping, and upon raising again noting any lack of continuity in the set-off. Any such break will, of course, indicate where a joint has not been formed, and the fault can be remedied by a little paper packing under that portion of the beading. If a small dent has been accidentally caused, the beading for an inch or two on each side of the defect should be rubbed down with a flat sandpaper block until the whole presents a smooth even surface, and then this portion packed up to the correct level.

The more completely fitted frames have four masking blinds attached which can be drawn and clamped in position around the negative to prevent any light action taking place except where required. With frames not so fitted the plate surrounding the negative must be protected with sheets of thin red or black paper.

Most of the frames in use in this country are designed to turn into the vertical position for exposure, and care should be taken in turning not to jar the frame against any stops that are provided. Excessive local heat must also be avoided, and cool air currents passing over a warm glass prevented; in a word, the natural and obvious precautions for glass should be taken.

An indication of maximum pressure and of contact between negative and plate is afforded by the appearance of the plate through the negative, the formation of "Newton's rings," and the change in sound of the motor exhaust.

A very common mistaken impression is that continued application of power will continuously and almost indefinitely increase the pressure. Even if a perfect vacuum could be obtained there would be a maximum pressure of about 14 lb per square inch, which, though perhaps more than necessary for our purpose, is not excessive. If the power operating the pump were doubled or increased a hundred times, the pressure applied to the negative would not be increased beyond the above figure; with ordinary apparatus the maximum pressure irrespective of applied power does not exceed 10 or 11 lb per square inch over the whole surface.

Further, it must be remembered that the pressure is equal on both sides of the glass, which is consequently not subjected to any strain tending to cause breakage. If, however, the negative glass is curved it tends to become flattened until it conforms to the frame glass and both are then subjected to stresses which in excessive cases result in breakage. Again, if some small obstruction is allowed to remain between the two glasses the total pressure for several square inches finds its resistance in a single point and the weaker of the two glasses will probably break.

A vacuum pressure gauge on the pump is often requested by users but is of little practical value. As shown above there is no reason whatever in attempting to observe and check what is impossible—excessive pressure. If the gauge is intended to indicate when pressure is obtained over the whole plate it is liable to be very misleading, for if an obstruction is formed at the outlet of the frame such as caused by a piece of masking paper, or a pocket formed by a smooth rubber blanket, then the gauge will show a reading which is not a true indication of the pressure which is applied to the negative and plate.

If breakages continually occur, the reduction of pressure to a few pounds per square inch is not only a very haphazard and doubtful remedy, but will result in a great deal of unnecessary loss of contact. Assuming proper attention regarding cleanliness of both glasses, the cause will be owing to the use of either paper for masking purposes *between* the two glasses, or poor quality and curved negative glass. If masking is necessary in this position only the thinnest tin-foil should be used. Paper or the thicker tin-foil sometimes employed is sufficiently thick, particularly where overlapping at the corners, to cause breakages when used with efficient frames and exhaust equipment.

Imperfect contact frequently occurs when using plates with bent-over edges which have not been flattened out. The area where trouble is found is a strip about half an inch inside the actual bend. This difficulty appears to be taken as insurmountable in many cases, but a little thought will show that the effect is caused by the edge of the plate being forced up towards the negative or the frame glass and acting as a lever to press down the portion of metal immediately inside the plate bend. In view of the fact that equal pressure is applied over the whole area, and to satisfy the mechanically minded, a further explanation could be given, but it would be rather lengthy and beside the point. The above is exactly what takes place and the obvious remedy is to prevent the plate edge being pressed up to the same level as the printing surface. Several strips of strawboard or hard felt can be laid along the bevelled edge for this purpose. The use of a thick felt pad under the printing surface is quite ineffective and useless. Several sheets of stout strawboard are also often tried, but they are only a partial remedy.

The ideal illuminant for printing on metal is one giving powerful and parallel rays of an equal intensity over the whole area to be covered. Sunlight is impracticable in this country though it is used extensively in suitable climates. (Special frames without overhead gear are made for use with sunlight.) There are various types of lamp which can be used, the most general being single- or multi-arc open type. One lamp is considered sufficient for use where negatives up to, say, 20 in. or 24 in. square are to be exposed singly, two or more being used for larger areas. The use of several arc lamps on one frame is a departure from the ideal and is a compromise between the advantages of single-point illumination and the excessively long exposure which would follow the increased lamp distance at which even covering would be obtained over a large plate. High-power single open arc lamps of 50 amperes or more are enabling much larger areas to be covered without seriously increasing exposure times. They have the further advantage that when used with

EIGHT-CARBON ARC LAMP AND TRIPOD STAND

small negatives exposure time can be reduced to a very short period. If, owing to the use of a very large frame, it is decided to use two such lamps, these may be connected in series on, say, a 220-volt supply and the total consumption should approximate 40 amperes. Banks of mercury vapour tubes, though their use is frequently advised or queried, must be considered obsolete for purposes other than printing down under conditions where the avoidance of heat is one of the main considerations. Even here the preference is of questionable justification, though it persists in certain quarters. The use of such lamps causes frequent trouble owing to the spread of light behind the opaque negative dots, particularly with dry plates, and if, for one of the many reasons which arise in practice and cannot always be rectified immediately, there is a small area of imperfect contact between negative and plate, the mercury vapour lamp will certainly not give the best possible result in the circumstances, but will definitely make the worst of the trouble. On the other hand, the single-point lamp will throw a fairly well-defined point of light on the plate and if the loss of contact is not too serious the result will with careful manipulation be satisfactory. Local loss of contact must of course be rectified if possible when observed, but such occasions often arise as when the only plate available for a rush job has a bad kink which cannot be entirely removed previous to coating or is not flattened out under pressure in the frame.

The enclosed arc lamp which gives a very actinic light and is used extensively in process shops is not recommended for photo-litho on account of the limited covering power and the difficulty of positioning the lamp opposite any point of a large frame. Much more cumbersome suspension gear is necessary than for, say, an open type 8-carbon lamp which can be mounted on a light and easily adjustable tripod.

The statement that the enclosed arc possesses a greater actinic value refers to black and white photography and printing on metal. At the time of writing these notes, experiments are in progress which have as their aim the production of an open arc which has a greater proportion of blue violet and ultra-violet. If the present expectation materializes there should be a very decided improvement in production times, and no doubt justification will be afforded for a wide adoption of still higher amperages. There is also the possibility of development in the gas discharge type of illuminant, but there are certain disadvantages attached to these, and their eventual use is at present a matter of speculation.

When all apparatus has been installed and tested, the standard exposure must be found, that is, the exposure to be given with a good quality clear negative and with average conditions regarding preparation of the plate and illumination. The variable factors governing exposure are—type and general density of the negative, type of lamp and distance from the frame, thickness of coating, condition of the solution, and relative humidity of the atmosphere. As a guide, the following set of conditions will require about 2 minutes' exposure—a wet collodion line negative 15 in. × 12 in., a zinc plate with medium photo grain, albumen solution made as previously described and one to three days old, whirling speed of 100 r.p.m., plate dried without overheating, a correctly adjusted 50-ampere single-arc lamp 24 in. from the frame, and relative humidity of 50 per cent.

Direct dry-plate negatives generally require slightly longer exposure than wet plates, but it must be remembered that the exposure time is much more critical.

A solution which has been freshly made will require an exposure slightly in excess of normal. Exposures remain constant with solutions of a few hours to two days old, and thereafter for a few days a limited increase of sensitivity will be noted, but advantages regarding ease of development will be proportionately lost. With a large negative the lamp must be further removed from the frame to obtain even illumination and the exposure increased accordingly, remembering that a lamp at 40 in. from the frame necessitates an exposure four times that required when the lamp is at 20 in. (See notes regarding lamp distances for camera—page 33.) When a stationary frame is being used it is a good plan to mark the floor at various distances from the frame, making a note of the standard exposures for each.

Should the negative have been over-exposed in the making or the lines slightly veiled, due to a dozen reasons including the ever-recurring "poor copy," or should one corner be stained, as frequently happens if insufficient care is given in the studio, the exposure to metal will have to be increased accordingly. If the additional exposure is required on part of the negative only, the remainder can be masked out for this period with pieces of moistened tin-foil placed on the front of the frame glass.

A thicker albumen coating (which also increases the necessary exposure) is advisable in cases such as a negative of inadequate density or with numerous minute pin-holes too general to paint out. A thicker coating may generally be assumed to give more contrast—extremely fine scratches or pin-holes produce images with such a weak hold on the plate that they can be developed away without serious damage to the image proper.

The exposure when printing screen negatives usually requires considerably more judgment, for in addition to the previously mentioned variable factors there is unfortunately, and in many cases unnecessarily, a variation in the general density of negatives and in their fidelity to the copy. Sets of direct colour-separated screen negatives which have been retouched by air-brush, pencil and brush, etc., require particular attention. With varying negatives no hard and fast rule can be laid down regarding the best method of procedure in all cases, and again we can only emphasize the importance of rigidly adhering to standard methods so far as possible, and keeping any modifications definitely under control; that is, the operator should always be sure of his methods and know exactly what results will follow variation in procedure.

The total exposure is usually ascertained by comparison of the denser portions of the screen negative with the corresponding light tones of the copy. A wet collodion negative which is correctly "high-lighted" (i.e. with the high-light formation showing the merest suggestion of a transparent dot) can be given a full exposure slightly in excess of that suggested for line work. If the shadow dots are too weak and a full exposure would result in the corresponding portions of the print becoming over-exposed and "thickened," a compromise may be effected and particular care taken during development; or preferably a thinner coating may be used. A thinner coating helps the small dots of light tones to be retained with normal exposure without unduly increasing the weight of the shadows: in effect it helps to make a good print from a too contrasty negative.

A negative with the high-lights insufficiently dense can be made to give a better result than might be expected by whirling the plate rather slower to obtain a thicker coating, and then increasing the exposure. This also must not be overdone, otherwise the plate will have a shorter life on the machine. In fact, we hesitate to suggest these departures, and trust that readers will rarely have occasion to make such alterations.

Careful attention should be given to humidity conditions, for a negative requiring an exposure time of, say, 3 minutes at 55 per cent relative humidity would possibly require 5 minutes at 35 per cent. If control of humidity is contemplated so much the better, otherwise variation of exposure time is necessary. Hunter-Penrose Ltd. supply an efficient and cheap hygrometer from which readings can be taken over a period to form an exposure table or graph for future guidance. Providing every precaution is taken to maintain standard conditions in other respects, together with a full period of, say, 10 minutes for drying, a note can be made of the printing exposures found necessary for a given screen negative at varying humidities. This table will be found of great use in estimating the correct exposures throughout the climatic variations to which we are continuously subjected.

Where the work consists of the printing of several negatives on one machine plate and at one operation, any allowances for varying qualities of negative will have to be made entirely by varying the exposures, but uniformity of results can occasionally be assisted by selective development. Careful examination of the several negative images will indicate those which can stand only a minimum exposure. A note should be made of these and the remainder graded off according to their respective printing qualities. Those not requiring maximum exposure are masked-off after the estimated periods by placing moistened tin-foil on the outside of the frame glass. This method may be put to further account in the case of either flat or contrasty negatives. With the former the middle and denser negative tones can be masked off after normal exposure and the exposure through the clear portions allowed to continue for a short period. With a contrasty negative the high-lights would be given an increased exposure in the same way. For this particular form of "faking" some red- or orange-coloured powder in sufficient water to form a paste will prove more easily applicable, particularly where numerous small portions require holding back. This necessitates added cleaning, for the frame will get into a very dirty condition if much of this work is done; but if a better print results than can be obtained with a straight exposure, then the end justifies the means. Local masking is only permissible for a small proportion of the total exposure: if the added exposures are too long an outline image of the tin-foil or paint will be superimposed, particularly if a stationary single-arc lamp is employed. Reliance on the possibilities of local variation of exposure is easily overdone and quickly leads to its adoption as standard practice instead of being a means of dealing with an emergency. Every effort must be made to get correct and properly balanced negatives in the first place. It must also be borne in mind that when duplication work has to be done, such faking in printing down is definitely ruled out.

As previously mentioned, the exposure for direct dry plates has to be judged still more critically, for variations even to a small degree are noticeably effective, due to the characteristics of the film. The edges of lines have not an abrupt change from clear to opaque film; the gelatine film as previously explained has an appreciable thickness and the image is incorporated *in* the film, whereas the wet collodion image is more stencil-like and built on the film surface. The gradation from opacity to clear gelatine film varies with the care expended and—more particularly—the methods adopted in the making, i.e. direct or indirect, methods of obtaining high-light results, etc. While a good dry-plate negative has a formation closely resembling that obtained with wet collodion it will always be found that between opaque and clear gelatine film there is this lack of abrupt contrast, and the effect when printing is that with a prolonged exposure the light action spreads under any veiled fringe surrounding the opaque dots. This effect is accentuated by reason of the grained printing surface, with the final result that unless proper precautions are taken lines get thickened and the shadow dots of a screen negative become almost ineffectual and a solid is presented where should be, say, a three-quarter tone; or, in shop parlance, the shadow detail "gets bunged." At the other end of the scale the slight veiling of the clear high-light dots will retard the light action, with a consequent loss and reduction in size of the smallest printed dots.

A dry-plate negative judged by wet-plate appearances may at first sight be expected to give with normal treatment a print with a full range of tones and faithfully reproducing the original, but, as explained, there are certain variations in the light action which result in a more contrasty print. The photographer must be acquainted with these points, and make negatives accordingly with a good firm dot in the shadows and a rather more open high-light formation than is necessary with wet collodion. Such negatives will permit of standard methods throughout with the exception perhaps of a slightly increased exposure.

It may again be remarked here that it is possible for a dry-plate negative which has been made by contact from a screen positive to approach very closely to the printing characteristics of a wet collodion negative. The same applies but in a lesser degree to a reduced and intensified negative which has been obtained from a good copy not necessitating forced high-lighting manipulations.

SECTION 2. INKING

The exposed plate has an image consisting of insoluble albumen, the remainder of the coating or the parts unaffected by white light still being in the original soluble condition. Consequently, if the plate were placed in water at this stage the soluble coating could be washed away, leaving the hardened or light-affected image of albumen. This is termed the basic image, but in itself is not sufficient to form a satisfactory lithographic image. Therefore, before developing the plate it is coated with a thin film of special ink. The care taken in this operation is of great importance. There are three general methods of application, viz. liquid ink applied by rubbing; liquid ink applied with a composition roller; or a fairly hard ink applied with a smooth nap roller.

The first has the advantage of speed and ease of application, particularly where large plates are concerned, but a thicker albumen coating is necessitated, and this will tend to reduce the life of the plate on the machine. The appearance of the developed image does not so closely resemble or indicate the appearance of the finished print on paper on account of the greyness of the ink and is consequently a little more difficult to judge for strength in cases where judgment is necessary and critical. This ink can either be obtained in liquid form from photo-litho supply houses, or be made by reducing good photo-litho ink with thin "wash-out" solution or pure freshly manufactured turpentine.

A sufficient quantity of ink to cover the required area is sprinkled on the plate and quickly spread over the whole surface with a pad made of dry, smooth rag free from fluff. Too much pressure must not be applied, otherwise the albumen coating on the peaks of the grain is liable to get damaged. The rubbing is continued with clean rags until the plate presents a smooth even surface without heavy streaks, and then it is allowed to stand for a few minutes before developing to allow the solvents to evaporate completely.

With the second method the ink need not be quite so thin as above, and is applied by rolling in opposite directions with a composition roller not too heavily charged. Although this method is extensively used it has little to commend it, and better results would be obtained by changing over to the third and following method, which, taking everything into consideration, gives the most satisfactory results providing due care is taken. Whether or not the extra labour is justified is a matter for individual decisions—class of work, length of run, etc., being taken into consideration.

Photo-litho ink (not to be confused with photo-transfer ink) is specially made for the purpose and has a fairly hard consistency, but it can mostly be worked without reducing or "letting down," and should in fact be used in this manner if possible. The most satisfactory roller is a "fine nap" about 12 in. in length and should be well prepared or conditioned as described later.

A small quantity of ink is placed on the roller and by use of the inking slab spread evenly over the whole surface, taking care that excess ink does not collect at the edges. It is most important that the roller is not overcharged. The surface of the plate is rolled up in all directions until a thin, even, hard film of ink is obtained. As much pressure as possible must be applied in order to get the ink well into the grain, but it is not necessary to grip the handles unduly. This method obviously entails more and harder work at this stage but definite advantages follow later, for each line or dot of the basic image will be protected by a really firm and black coating of ink which will easily withstand the subsequent treatment and present a general appearance comparable to the finished print. Further, the albumen coating can be kept as thin as other factors will allow. This is important when aiming at plates which will stand up to long runs.

Points to watch with this method are as follows. The ink must be fed to the plate gradually but firmly from a sparely charged roller; the ink film must not be too heavy; the roller must be used for this purpose only, and must be kept absolutely free from moisture.

Periodical scraping is necessary to keep the roller free from dirt and old ink—once a day will usually be sufficient. Care must be taken that water does not get on to the surface of the plate while inking. An obvious caution, perhaps, but it frequently happens that after hurried work there are still patches of moisture on the back of the plate after removal from the vacuum frame. Water can thus quite easily get on to the rolling-up table and so to the roller and plate surface. If this happens it will be evidenced immediately by a small white patch where ink already deposited is picked up again by the roller. Rolling must be stopped immediately and the plate fanned dry. The roller should be worked on the ink slab for a minute or so before recommencing on the plate. In the majority of cases sufficient albumen coating will be left on the plate to take ink and develop away subsequently.

The rolling-up table is often the cause of uneven and streaky inking due to ridges and warped boards. This table should be of rigid and substantial structure with a covering such as thick linoleum or sheet iron, either of which makes an excellent surface. An iron bed plate can be employed with advantage, but most firms will consider this an unnecessary expense.

A new nap roller must be conditioned before using. If this work can be left to an experienced lithographer so much the better, but the following instructions if carried out carefully will result in a surface which will readily distribute the ink with a minimum amount of trouble. The work should be put in hand some time before the roller is required, for complete conditioning cannot be hurried. First rub Russian tallow well into the skin while holding the roller in front of gentle heat. Two or three more applications are advisable at intervals of a day or so. Then roll up with equal parts of tallow and medium litho varnish. As this is gradually absorbed add more varnish until only varnish is used. Scrape the roller and roll up with photo-litho ink and varnish for at least half an hour each day for a week, gradually increasing the proportion of ink until only ink is used. Repeated scraping should also be given. One handle must be marked and the scraper always drawn towards this.

SECTION 3. DEVELOPING AND HAND WORK

The inked plate is placed under a jet of water or preferably completely immersed in a shallow tray. After a minute, or slightly longer if liquid ink has been used, development of the image can be commenced by gently rubbing the surface of the plate with cotton-wool. This should not be allowed to collect much ink and must be continually washed under the water jet. Development is continued until the image appears sharp and clean over the whole area. If the plate has been fully exposed it should withstand a final cleaning with sponge or felt, but it must not be inferred that this latter procedure is invariably necessary. The advised composition of the albumen solution ensures that the unexposed parts develop quite freely under a wide margin of working conditions. If, however, the image should fail to clear immediately it is not necessary to scrub vigorously: the plate may be soaked for a period and if it is still obstinate it can be drained slightly and a very weak solution of ammonia or 1 per cent solution of sodium bicarbonate applied. Better still, a small quantity of the albumen solution may be used. This has sufficient ammonia content for the purpose, and it will be found to have a less vigorous and penetrating action. Following this treatment the plate must be thoroughly washed.

Some of the causes of difficult development have already been suggested, but they may be summarized as follows—

1. Oxidized or dirty plate.
2. Insufficient washing of plate after acid treatment.
3. Albumen coating too thin for the texture of grain. The thin coating might be due to the composition of the solution or carelessness in making up; insufficient draining of the plate before coating; whirling too rapidly; or the use of poor quality albumen, and working to a formula instead of density.
4. Old solution. To be on the safe side, solution which is over a week old should not be used.
5. Too much ink, or the use of ink through which water cannot readily penetrate sufficiently for developing purposes.
6. Insufficient ammonia in the albumen solution, particularly in conjunction with any of the following.
7. Over-heating of the plate. The plate should not be permitted to get more than "hand-warm."
8. The dried coating being exposed to damp air.
9. Unsuitable negative or over-exposure.
10. Light fog from general lighting. This, by the way, is frequently blamed first, whereas it is usually the most unlikely

cause of trouble even where for multi-printing purposes the plate has to stand for a period of anything up to $2\frac{1}{2}$ hours between coating and development.

11. Too long a period between coating and developing. No fixed limit can be given, as this depends entirely on atmospheric conditions and thickness of coating, etc. When prolonged periods with high humidity are unavoidable, a protective coating is sometimes employed by rubbing over the following—

Turpentine	.	.	.	.	.	300 parts
Castor oil	.	.	.	.	.	2 ,,
Paraffin .	.	.	.	.	.	2 ,,
Castile soap	.	.	.	.	.	1 part

This coating must be removed with turpentine prior to inking. While our personal experience does not confirm any real advantage attaching to this treatment, it might be of use in isolated circumstances. We prefer to endeavour to attack the trouble at its source by reducing the relative humidity and increasing exposure.

It is not difficult to watch all these points, and careful attention makes all the difference between consistently good work and indefinite or doubtful results.

Many operators still imagine that if a plate starts to develop immediately and without difficulty it necessarily indicates too thick a coating or under-exposure. This is quite wrong and if correct procedure has been followed the plate *should* develop freely and the image will be much sharper, cleaner and just as firm as one requiring prolonged and vigorous treatment.

A very common fault which may arise immediately development commences, is spreading of the ink, particularly in the shadows. The reason is the use of too much ink or too soft ink. The remedy is obvious for the next plate, but if the job is wanted in a hurry and the existing plate must be made as satisfactory as possible, it must be soaked in water for fifteen minutes or so, and then development continued very carefully, keeping the cotton-wool as free from loose ink as possible. The print is finished off with a piece of fluff-free and well-washed felt, using a "plucking" or lifting action without rubbing the felt backwards and forwards over the image which would probably spread the ink still more.

After the plate has had a general development it might in a few isolated instances be improved with a little selective development, but it must be remembered that it should be the aim of those concerned to render this procedure unnecessary by careful work in the studio and hand work on the negative, particularly where this has to be printed down more than once. However, if it is decided that a portion of the print is too heavy it can be reduced by applying albumen solution, as previously suggested for an obstinate plate, and development continued with felt, soft sponge, or a small hogs-hair brush of a suitable size according to the work to be done. Considerable restraint must be exercised, otherwise the ink on top of the albumen image will get rubbed off, making the work appear rotted, and probably the paper impression will be quite different from the appearance of the work on the plate: parts of the image which appeared sufficiently light on the plate owing merely to rubbing away the ink may build up to almost original strength during the run on the press. On the other hand, these parts may become so affected by the etching operations that they get still weaker and detail becomes indefinite or lost, so it is a matter of patience where reduction of the print cannot be avoided. Allow the ammonia in the albumen solution to take effect around the edges of the dots rather than by scrubbing vigorously, which would falsify the apparent printing value of the plate.

In cases of a suspected weak image, careful and light development may be followed by one or two minutes' application of a 10 per cent solution of chrome alum, which has a hardening action on the albumen image. Unfortunately, however, this treatment sometimes has a detrimental effect on the tenacity of the ink.

To dry the plate it should be dabbed with a clean chamois leather and placed on the whirler or fanned dry. Careless and hurried drying by heat is often the cause of trouble, particularly with screen subjects, as beads of water collect on the image and get warm, consequently dissolving the edges of lines or dots which were previously insoluble while cold water was used. Obviously then, these portions of the image will be weaker and the albumen which has been dissolved will, when the water finally dries, be deposited in the form of a slight scum on the clean zinc. This effect would be very noticeable with a print which will not stand the normal development.

Drying too slowly will result in oxidization. The application of reasonable heat *after* drying is quite in order: commonly and aptly termed "baking," it tends to harden the albumen image. An exposure to strong light at this stage is often credited with a further hardening action. No such action occurs, however. Possibly a slight effect would follow if the plate were first soaked in a 5 per cent solution of ammonium bichromate.

At this stage any spotting or other hand work is carried out where necessary, using litho chalk, litho drawing ink or stippling mediums. While all such hand work is now eliminated whenever possible by work on the negatives, it is occasionally necessary or easier to strengthen a tone on the printed image. The shading medium is, perhaps, the most commonly used for strengthening general tones, but an air-brush, if handled with considerable skill and experienced judgment, gives excellent results. This must only be used after much practice on work which may be considered experimental. When using a shading medium care must be taken to select a design and texture of stipple which will not create a pattern with the screen image. If a half-tone medium is employed, the angle should be so adjusted relative to the angle of the printed half-tone that the least evidence of pattern is noticeable.

Litho chalk may be used for detail work. Such work on the light tones must be watched very carefully as it tends to become much more obvious when printing on the press. Litho drawing ink applied with brush or stippling pen is used for the finest detail corrections.

When a plate has received hand work in addition to the photographic image, complaints are frequently heard that such work does not hold so well as on a plate straight from the graining department. This is usually attributed (by departments other than the printing down) to a thin film of the "sensitizing solution" remaining on the plate. The metal printer, if he has done his job correctly, knows definitely that not a trace of the albumen solution remains on the plate and puts the trouble down to oxidization caused through the plate having to stand for a lengthy period while awaiting attention. He is frequently perfectly right, but the real cause of this partial insensitivity to hand work after photo-litho treatment is the obscure chemical action which takes place between the bichromate and the metal. A simple solution of ammonium bichromate and water applied to a freshly grained plate would result in the same complaint, consequently no amount of washing after development would eliminate the trouble. However, the plate can very easily be brought back to its original sensitivity or affinity by the application of a 5–10 per cent solution of iron perchloride after development and before final washing. This solution will not affect the image, as frequently occurs with the usual acid treatment, and its use may be adopted as standard treatment if any hand work is likely to be added. It is, of course, essential with a plate gummed immediately after graining (as mentioned on page 168) and not subsequently treated with acid.

SECTION 4. FINISHING

The modern method of preparing a plate ready for the machine is taking quite an unreasonable time in being generally adopted. In many shops the time-wasting and laborious process of gumming, hand rolling, weak etching, washing out, re-rolling and final etching, etc., is still carried out in varying degrees or combinations on each and every plate, quite irrespective of reason for the image being subjected to such lengthy and sometimes ruinous treatment. Any photo-litho plate having passed through the preceding processes satisfactorily will have a good strong acid-resisting ink image over a well-hardened albumen image, and the portions of the zinc corresponding to the whites of the subject should be absolutely clean with not a trace of foreign matter or oxidization. Now, how is this going to be improved by such treatment as mentioned above? Not at all. More often than not the shadow detail gets "bunged," the middle tones become heavy and the high-lights rotted. Further, as this distortion of the original print varies and values of a colour job are often entirely upset, the artist responsible for negative correction and passing the prints on metal is given quite a false idea of the effect of his retouching and estimated modifications to make for his next set.

It must be pointed out that the photo-litho image obtained from a negative is not formed in the same way as a pure lithographic image, nor does it depend on the affinity of metal to greasy substances. Although it is but little appreciated as yet, it is possible to produce perfectly satisfactory results by photo-printing direct to an etched, gummed and washed plate. This statement would be considered a heresy by most lithographers, but it well defines one of the essential differences between the two processes. The strength of the albumen image depends on a physical tenacity rather than the chemical affinity which is a fundamental principle of pure lithography.

Certainly there are isolated plates which require either full or partial treatment before etching—plates with heavy portions of hand work, weak images together with possibly oxidized or otherwise doubtful metal requiring a more vigorous or corrosive etch—but for normal straightforward photo-litho work the following procedure is sufficient and retains the full range of values as printed through the negative. After the plate has been developed and dried, the image is dusted with French chalk, and a soft sponge soaked in any good etch of full strength is applied to the plate for the required period, usually two or three minutes. There are several excellent proprietary etches available such as "Atzol," "Litholene," etc., or the following may be used: ammonium nitrate 1 part, ammonium biphosphate 1 part, water or weak gum solution 20 parts.

The etch is often applied to the plate immediately after developing and before drying, but this is definitely not recommended unless the operator is thoroughly sure of his methods and is not in any sense experimenting. For one thing, the etch becomes diluted to an unknown extent and quite probably never reaches the metal in the minute dots of the strongest tones. Consequently these portions will eventually thicken during the run unless the plate receives a second and correct etch. Further, although the light-hardened albumen is considered insoluble, it is still subject to water absorption, and there is a possibility—rather remote, perhaps—of the diluted etch penetrating and weakening the albumen, or the adhesion of the albumen, at the dot periphery. The etch must be applied thoroughly, but not roughly. It is most essential that a complete action takes place around every dot. Merely flowing the etch over the plate is useless and will result in eventual thickening owing to the etch being repelled to some extent by the grease of the image, leaving a minute ring of only partially etched metal around each dot.

The plate is washed and dried after etching and fresh gum

solution (about one part of gum arabic to five parts water) is applied with a clean soft sponge, the film being wiped to a minimum thickness with smooth rag or mutton cloth damped with gum solution. A second application of gum, well wiped into the grain of the plate and then dried, is an advised precaution, though not absolutely essential. If this second gumming is adopted as standard practice the first application may be made without necessarily drying the plate. If the gum coating is too thick it is liable to crack and reticulate during drying and will pull away portions of the surface ink, paricularly in the solids. Should this defect occur, the plate should be washed, thinly gummed, washed out with asphaltum solution, damped and rolled up with a fairly hard ink.

If the plate is not to be used for several days it should be thinly gummed, dried, and washed out with asphaltum solution, wiped over with a damp sponge, gummed and dried before storing. The storing racks must always be in the driest possible place; if plates under gum are allowed to stand even for a short period in a damp place the gum will absorb moisture, possibly become acidified and certainly allow the plate to become oxidized. It is claimed that gum solution to which has been added a small proportion of ammonium bichromate is more effective. This coating, after drying, is exposed to the light of an arc lamp for a few minutes. The plate is then washed well and a thin coating of ordinary gum solution applied.

Plates on which important hand work and corrections have been made must be treated in accordance with standard litho practice, i.e. dusted with chalk, gummed thinly and dried, washed out with special "wash-out solution" or asphaltum solution, and again fanned dry. (Some workers use pure turpentine with a little water; while this is a distinct departure from general practice it appears thoroughly effective and to cause no trouble for the following operations.) The plate is damped and rolled up, using a nap roller and black litho ink to which has been added about 25 per cent of re-transfer ink. Only skill and experience will enable this work to be carried through without over-inking and yet build up a sufficient resist for the litho etch which is applied for two or three minutes, followed by gumming and drying and final wash-out ready for the machine.

To obtain the best possible results from a photo-litho plate, the machine minder must be extremely critical regarding correct pressure, and should allow the work to ink up gradually, keeping the rollers sparely charged while running through the "wasters." The ink should be as stiff as circumstances permit, and the damping water should have only the slightest trace of acidity. If the damping water is over-acidified, corrosion will occur, while exact neutrality or slight alkalinity leaves the albumen image in a weaker state and more subject to wear by friction. It is common practice to add an ounce or so of gum solution to each gallon of damping water; about 10 minims of phosphoric acid should also be added. The fountain water should be changed daily.

SECTION 5. PHOTOGRAPHIC SET-OFFS

While these are not strictly associated with photo-litho the inclusion of a tested method will undoubtedly prove of assistance to many departments. If, for instance, a key drawing only of a map or similar design is provided, this can be photographically printed to each of the several plates, giving images which will not ink up or interfere in any way with the work of the lithographic draughtsman.

The sensitive solution consists of equal parts ammonio-citrate of iron 20 per cent solution, and potassium ferricyanide 20 per cent solution. This should be kept in the dark. The metal plate is cleaned in the usual way and very thoroughly washed after any acid treatment. The above solution is flowed over the plate and dried on the whirler. Exposure to the negative is not critical—say 3–6 minutes with an eight-carbon arc lamp at 20 inches. Immediately after exposure a 5 per cent solution of iron perchloride is quickly and evenly flowed over the plate, which is then thoroughly washed. If an unwanted blue stain appears on the background it is of little consequence, but may be removed with a few drops of ammonia in water. If this clearing is accidentally taken too far and the image appears weak it may be strengthened again by flowing over with the iron perchloride solution. After quickly drying, the plate is ready for hand work with liquid litho-ink or crayon, the work being subsequently dusted with chalk and bitumen and washed out, etc., as in standard lithographic practice.

SECTION 6. ALUMINIUM

When using aluminium the general methods and precautions necessary for zinc are applicable. There are certain differences in the properties of the two metals which give rise to the previously mentioned diversity of opinion as to which is the better metal for general work. While zinc is by far the more generally adopted there are many firms that adhere to the use of aluminium, claiming that the image is less likely to spread under certain adverse printing conditions. We believe, however, that with correct treatment throughout graining, storing, preparation and printing, equally good results can be obtained with either metal.

Certain alterations are necessary in the various solutions; the cleaning solution can be one of the following—

> 3 per cent Hydrochloric acid,
> 5 per cent Citric acid,
> 5 per cent Acetic acid,
> 3 per cent Nitric acid with 1 per cent Hydrofluoric acid.

After washing, the plate is flowed over with a weak solution of ammonia and water and again washed ready for coating.

The albumen solution will have to be somewhat thicker than that used under similar conditions for zinc, due to identical graining treatment producing a slightly different texture. The addition of 1 part of fish glue to each 100 parts of albumen solution will serve the purpose, or preferably the quantity of water in the normal formula may be reduced—

Dried egg albumen .	. . 5 oz		160 g
Ammonium bichromate .	. 1¼ oz	or	40 g
Liquid ammonia 0·880	(approx.) 1 oz		32 c.c.
Distilled water up to	. 60–65 oz		2000 c.c.

The longer exposure which would be assumed necessary with the thicker solution is mostly rendered unnecessary by the greater reflective property of the aluminium surface.

Etching solution. Proprietary etches can be obtained suitable for both aluminium and zinc or for aluminium only. The principal agent of most of these etches is phosphoric acid, and a suitable etch may be made with 1 part phosphoric acid, 30 parts weak gum solution (12° Baumé) and 1 part 20 per cent solution ammonium bichromate; or, sodium phosphate 1 part, sodium nitrate 1 part, water 50 parts, phosphoric acid 2 parts.

It must be remembered that while both zinc and aluminium are readily affected by damp, the latter is particularly susceptible and extreme care must be taken at all times.

SECTION 7. PRINTING ON STONE

This procedure appears to be very little used in this country, but many continental establishments find real justification for the retention of litho stones for certain classes of work. If hand transfers are required, a print on stone certainly yields excellent impressions for the purpose, and there are other definite advantages, such as the possibility of fine etching for colour correction, and the ease with which repeated alterations can be made for cartographical work, etc.

To coat the stone with bichromated albumen solution a whirler of special construction is employed, or failing this the stone may be coated by either pouring on a small quantity of solution and spreading evenly with a flat pad of plush, or placing the stone at a suitable angle and flowing the solution over the surface after first treating it with warm water. An electric blower giving a current of warm air is used for drying purposes. The coating will require to be rather thicker than that found satisfactory for plates.

The arc lamp is of the type which throws the light downwards as stones are usually exposed in a horizontal position with the negative laid face down on the stone and a heavy sheet of glass on top to ensure contact. Special frames can of course be employed but these need be of only simple design such as a table with a spring loaded glass top and a stone support below which can be raised and lowered by a centre screw adjustment.

If collodion negatives are being employed the film may be stripped and stuck down to the stone surface with oil. This obviates the use of any frame or cover glass. The oil must be removed with turpentine before inking.

Inking, developing and etching are as described for plates, with the exception that diluted nitric acid and gum are used for the etch.

SECTION 8. DIRECT PROJECTION

Printing on metal by means of light projection through a fine-screen negative has been practised to a limited extent for many years, but recently improvements have been made in the apparatus available regarding optical, electrical, and mechanical features, which are resulting in renewed interest.

There are two general systems—one employing bichromated colloid and the other an emulsion having a sensitivity comparable with ordinary dry plates. The latter may be a silver-gelatine emulsion, which can be tanned during development and then treated with warm water to leave a stencil for one of the reversal processes (see Chap. XIII) or a double coating of bichromated colloid and silver emulsion with a waterproof layer between. The silver image is developed to form a negative, and the underlying bichromate coating can subsequently be exposed to an arc lamp. Although the equipment for this process can be fairly simple on account of the practicability of using a reflector as in transparency projection, there are objections which appear to justify a preference for projecting direct on to bichromated colloids.

The main features of a machine for this purpose include a suitable negative holder (say 12 in. × 10 in.), with aligning device, a very powerful single-point illuminant and condenser system, projection lens, plate-holding apparatus (possibly including duplicating mechanism), and efficient cooling system.

The machine must be mounted on a vibration-free floor, and every possible precaution taken to avoid dust at all stages of manipulation. The negatives must be of maximum sharpness, and have a perfectly clear image on a dense ground. Exposure time depends not only on the design of the whole apparatus and type of coating, but on the degree of relative humidity, which can be kept to a fairly high level if it is essential to reduce exposure to a minimum. Very completely equipped apparatus is now being manufactured on the above lines, and operating satisfactorily for the production of first-class posters in colour. The machine being offered by the Monotype Corporation is a combined camera and projector, and in place of the previously used high-power single arc lamp with one rotating horizontal carbon, one of the new water-cooled extra high pressure arcs is used. This arc is about 25 mm in length, and is intensely brilliant: when fully developed commercially, it will doubtless play a very big part in all projection, and perhaps general photo-mechanical work, owing to its steadiness and high actinic value. It is claimed—with justification—that the characteristics of this illuminant enable a much sharper image to be obtained than is possible by other systems.

CHAPTER XII

DUPLICATE AND GROUP PRINTING

A VERY large proportion of commercial litho printing consists of duplicated designs or groups of different subjects in both single and multi-colour. The oldest method of printing down on to small plates and then transferring has now been almost entirely superseded by direct photo-printing to the machine plate. This has the great advantage that each machine plate is an original with the consequent maximum sharpness, clearness of detail and increased life on the machine.

Such plates can be prepared in several ways and with varying degrees of assured accuracy according to the apparatus employed, or, failing any such special apparatus, the skill of the worker. Present-day requirements will not permit of lengthy and laborious methods, and wherever possible the necessary equipment for mechanical duplication is being installed. This will be described, but it is of interest to note the various ways and means devised before these modern conveniences became available, as such methods have still to be used extensively.

Presuming a colour job to be printed down in several positions on the machine plate, the copy is provided with the usual corner or centre register marks which of course appear on each negative. Each plate has first to be prepared with corresponding marks clearly defined in each of the several positions, and this is the most troublesome part of the procedure. They can be obtained in several ways: they may be transferred by means of set-off powder from a key plate or the first printing plate in a manner similar to that in use for transferring key impressions for litho drawing, or inking the register marks of the first plate and transferring by means of an offset proof press, or they may be obtained by means of a drawn key sheet and carbon paper, the impressed register marks being strengthened by ruling over with waterproof ink which would remain intact throughout the following washing and coating. Stout paper stencils can also be used for ruling the plate, or in the case of certain simple layouts it is quite practicable to rule each plate by direct measurement either before or after coating.

Probably the best of the drawn methods is to employ a sheet of thin soft zinc on which the groups of register marks are drawn to measurement or from a layout and then cut through with a stencil knife or similar tool. This sheet is firmly positioned over each of the litho plates in turn, and by means of a pointer the register marks are scribed on the plate surface. A very large number of normal register jobs can be completed by one of these metal stencils or guides before the perforations become too numerous, for those not required can be marked to avoid confusion.

A very definite way of obtaining the groups of register marks in their exact relative positions is by photo-printing. This probably takes longer, but is well worth while. The outlines of three suggested methods are as follows, the first being for group printing only.

1. Requires the use of both face-up and face-down frames. The negatives of the first colour are carefully positioned on the glass of the face-down frame and each secured with two or three small strips of gummed paper. After the first plate has been printed from these negatives they are masked out with thin tin-foil, leaving only the register marks exposed. A print of the register marks is then made on each of the remaining plates. These must be thoroughly developed and cleaned before storing to await re-coating and printing in the face-up frame.

2. Requires a sheet of glass the full size of the printing area

of the plate. This is flowed over or painted with a fairly hard black or red paint.[1] The necessary register marks can be cut through this coating with a sharp knife; the result is the equivalent of a full-size key negative and can be printed down to the required number of plates. The glass can be used for a great number of layouts without having to be cleaned and re-coated, for groups of cut register marks may be either painted out or covered with small pieces of tin-foil. The tin-foil should be used if there is a possibility of a further plate being required in the future from the same layout.

3. Also requires a sheet of glass, but the register marks are ruled in position with opaque paint, forming a positive which can be printed down by a bichromated gum process as follows—

A.	Gum arabic	.	.	.	. 5 oz	or	110 g
	Ammonia	.	.	.	. ½ oz		10 c.c.
	Water	.	.	.	. 25 oz		500 c.c.
B.	Ammonium bichromate	.	.	. 5 oz		or	100 g
	Ammonia	.	.	.	. ½ oz		10 c.c.
	Water	.	.	.	. 25 oz		500 c.c.

Add three parts of solution A to one part of B immediately before use. Coat and dry the plate and expose to the glass key positive. The printed register marks will be clearly visible and may be developed locally with sulphuric acid 1 part, glycerine 20 parts; or glacial acetic acid 1 part, glycerine 3 parts. The developer is cleaned away with methylated spirit and cotton-wool and the developed register marks inked up by rubbing with liquid ink (Vandyke ink, turpentine and re-transfer ink, or

[1] A good opaque coating may be obtained by use of fish glue as follows: Coat the glass plate with 2½ per cent ammonium bichromate solution 12 oz (360 c.c.), fish glue 2 oz (60 c.c.). Whirl dry and expose to the light of an arc lamp for a few minutes. Rinse and apply lead nitrate 4 oz (100 g), pot. ferricyanide 5 oz (125 g), water 80 oz (2000 c.c.). Rinse and blacken with diluted ammonium sulphide (not sodium sulphide). Two or three applications of the two intensifying solutions will be necessary. When dry, coat with clear cellulose varnish or any negative varnish.

waterproof drawing ink). The plate is placed in water and the gum stencil washed away: 1 per cent sulphuric or hydrochloric acid may be used to speed up this operation.

The register marks having been obtained by any of the foregoing methods, the plate is coated and placed in the face-up printing frame and the negative positioned over the first pair of printed register marks, the sighting being facilitated by scraping away a small portion of the film at the centre of each cross. After packing around the negative, masking, etc., the first exposure is made—providing that the negative has not moved during the process of obtaining contact. (Many operators will no doubt fully appreciate this latter remark.) The negative is repositioned and printed down the required number of times. Very good register can be obtained with careful workmanship, but there is always the risk of the coating being damaged, either by the edges of the glass while adjusting, in spite of paper strips for protection, or by moisture from the hands or breath. There are obviously many difficulties associated with sighting and maintaining registered position, particularly where the repeats exceed three or four; however, a large amount of work has been and is still being carried out in this manner or by some adaptation according to the type of frame used.

Very thin adhesive cellulose tape is now available, and operators consider this indispensable after having once tested its advantages in connexion with attachment of negatives to the printing surface.

When positioning negatives on the plate, an overhead light is of course essential: an orange or yellow lamp with suitable guard and flexible lead must be provided if the frame is not fitted with one of the extending and folding brackets which are now included on the latest models.

One of the first mechanical aids to ensure perfect registration and uniformity was the H.P. Register Model Vacuum Printing

Frame. This frame is a profitable acquisition and is being very extensively used in all parts of the world for duplicate, multi-design, and general printing-down processes. It consists essentially of two metal frames, the lower supporting the glass

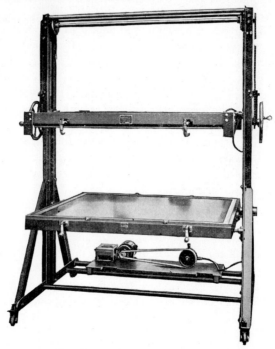

THE "H.P." REGISTER MODEL PRINTING FRAME

and the upper a rubber blanket with suitable gripper bars and centre supports to which is secured the machine plate. Special registering devices enable a negative to be secured to the lower frame exactly in any predetermined position relative to the centre of the frame and according to a drawn layout. The upper frame is independently rotatable to facilitate the attachment of the machine plate in a central position. The two frames can be clamped together in the usual manner and the air exhausted. Roller masking blinds can be adjusted to protect all portions of the plate not being exposed through the negative. After each exposure the registering device again comes into operation and the negative is adjusted in the next position. Should the

REGISTER DEVICE FOR REGISTER FRAME

work consist of several designs, all the negatives can be positioned on the frame and the whole exposed at one operation. An exclusive advantage of this frame is its ability to duplicate much larger negatives than the more elaborate mechanical duplicating machines.

The latest advances in this direction are machines such as the Repetex Plate Printing and Duplicating Machine, on which all movements and adjustments of the negative and plate are effected by mechanical means, thus obtaining the absolute maximum precision, uniformity and speed combined with extreme ease of operation.

With machines of this description one of the most important

THE "REPETEX" PLATE PRINTING AND DUPLICATING MACHINE

considerations is the method devised for the initial registering of the negative in the glass frame (usually removable) which is common to all duplicating machines. The Repetex has a patented device of unique design which allows the negative to be positioned in an approximately central position so that two micro-screw adjustable points can be brought quickly into perfect alignment with the negative register marks. These two points subsequently engage with two permanently aligned points on the machine, consequently each negative is brought into an exact location with the machine itself ready for adjustment to any part of the plate. When attaching the negative carrier to the machine it can be placed in any of the four positions of head to front, rear, left or right, thus ensuring mechanical accuracy of register for each plate and eliminating re-registering the negative for a reversal or quarter turn.

It is a great advantage to employ two carriers for quick change-over of negatives, and the Repetex method of registering enables this to be done without in any way affecting the exact mechanical precision.

The negative carrier is supported in a travelling frame which traverses the bed of the machine and is operated by a large hand wheel. The bed of the machine to which is attached the metal plate is adjustable lengthwise and is similarly controlled by hand wheel. Each adjusting wheel has two dials, one calibrated for inch adjustments and the other marked in clear well-separated divisions each representing a thousandth of an inch. The dials in their fixed positions give readings representing the position of the centre of the negative relative to the middle of the gripper edge of the plate, but the dials can be released and readjusted at any time to give a zero reading for the existing negative position ready for an immediate adjustment to the following position without calculation.

Contact is obtained by mechanical pressure, the whole centre structure being lowered by a hand wheel operating through a spring-controlled clutch. A compensating device is incorporated for a negative glass of uneven thickness. Negative glasses of any thickness can be employed without additional adjustment. The single-arc lamp is housed in an enclosed box which travels with the negative; this arc is extremely powerful and reduces exposure times to an average of two minutes.

"Printex Junior" Direct Mechanical Negative Printer

Almost in a class by itself is the "Printex Junior" Direct Mechanical Negative Printer, being manufactured by Pictorial Machinery Limited of London.

As can be seen by the illustration, this machine is very definitely precision built, which is necessary in a machine of this type, where accuracy in repeating a design over very large areas of plates and assuring the multiple plates are absolutely in register are essential.

The machine is fully equipped, incorporating its own lighting system and light control, a solid built-in register table with extra unit holders to accommodate various sizes of negatives up to 20 in. × 16 in.

It will be found that with all methods of repeat printing a variation in exposure time is necessary between the first and last prints. This is due not only to the "continued action" of the first exposures but also to the probable change in relative humidity caused by the heat of the arc lamp. This change will be more noticeable in small rooms.

Exact timing of multiple exposures—or, in point of fact, any exposure—can very rarely be accomplished under normal conditions, on account of the fluctuations in light intensity, which are inevitable. These fluctuations occur not only through the characteristics of the arc lamp itself, but on account of variations in the voltage of the power supply. It is well known, for instance, that when operating after normal working hours, exposures have to be generally reduced to 75 per cent of those given earlier. These variations are occurring continuously during the day, and the only satisfactory and sure method of timing exposures so that a known amount of light reaches the

"PRINTEX JUNIOR" DIRECT MECHANICAL NEGATIVE PRINTER

sensitive surface is to employ one of the integrating photo-electric meters which are now available. The photo-cell of these instruments receives light either direct from the arc lamp or from a limited reflecting surface, preferably on the same plane as the printing surface, and the light is transformed into energy which operates some form of meter or counting mechanism. With such a control it is obvious that exposure *time* is increased or decreased according to the actual light received by the subject.

A series of exposures can be made of identical value, and

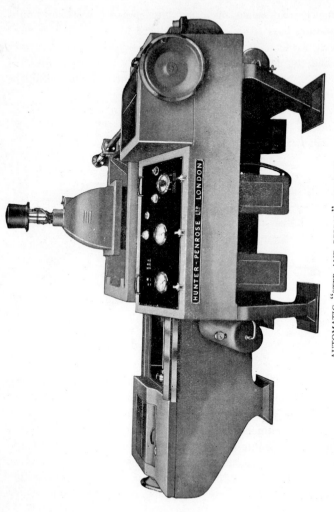

AUTOMATIC "STEP AND REPEAT" MACHINE

under- or over-exposure in ordinary work is entirely avoided, providing, of course, that a correct estimate has been made.

Most outstanding machine of the printing-down step and repeat type is perhaps the Hunter-Penrose Fully Automatic Machine, which has the negative registered in its carrier by a method similar to that described for the "Repetex" machine and thereafter exposes the negative at previously chosen positions about the plate. The sequence of steps is decided by punching holes in a chart, similar to a graph, which is actually a "plane" diagram of the driving thread of the machine. Electrical contacts, made through the punched holes to the surface of a metal drum which is directly mounted on the end of the thread, cause the carrier to stop in accordance with the holes punched.

All mechanical defects, such as backlash on the thread, and wear, are automatically taken up so that the machine can be relied upon to give absolute accuracy.

Once the controls, such as exposure time, number of exposures, vacuum contact and spacing have been set, the machine carries out the whole cycle of operations and completes the exposing of the plate surface.

The particular advantage of this machine, beyond that by which the operator in charge can be given time to prepare and mask the next negative to be printed down, is that every succeeding negative of a colour set must print down in register to that previously printed, ensuring absolute fit between the colours over the whole area. The operator is thereby relieved of this painstaking responsibility.

The output of such a machine is incomparable to the ancient transferring methods.

Light Meter

Such a control as the last two mentioned machines have fitted as standard, can, of course, be fitted to any earlier designed machines.

Until the real value of photo-electric cell control is properly appreciated the cost will perhaps be considered avoidable, and a more simple form of meter may have to be considered. In such cases one of the small direct-reading photo-electric exposure meters as used for ordinary photography can be a considerable help, although it only indicates the intensity of light at a given moment, and often has an appreciable time lag.

If, however, the meter is placed in a constant position near the original on the camera copyboard or on the printing frame, the lamps can be positioned (or adjusted, if a regulator is provided) so that the light produces a standard reading at the commencement of each exposure. The behaviour of lamps in good condition should be reasonably steady for the period of a normal exposure, and any excessive variation is indicated on the meter, so the operator has at least an opportunity of estimating the required modifications with a far greater assurance than by just giving so many minutes and "hoping for the best."

While it was stated earlier that hand-transferring is being largely superseded, it should be noted that mechanical transfer, using a special multi-transferring machine (Strachan & Henshaw), is being employed with entire success by many photo-litho establishments. The machine has been designed to reproduce the finest half-tone "originals" in exact register, and to eliminate the variations which are liable to occur with hand-transferring.

CHAPTER XIII

REVERSING

SURVEY Departments, etc., produce a great proportion of their plates by a reversing process, i.e. printing direct from a positive. For certain classes of work this obviates the necessity of making a negative and ensures the plate image being exactly the same size as the original, which may be a drawing either on transparent paper or white paper which will pass sufficient light for the purpose. The process is one requiring careful balance in determining the coating conditions and exposure, and the majority of departments work out their own modifications and alterations according to experience. Climatic conditions appear to have a definite bearing on the success or otherwise of any particular procedure. However, the following details have been recommended to departments in many parts of the world, and where variations have been found necessary to suit local conditions they are only in minor details.

Particular attention must be paid to the original to ensure that all the lines are as dense as possible. The following solution is filtered and flowed over the plate and dried on the whirler: fish glue 1 part; $2\frac{1}{2}$ per cent solution ammonium bichromate 4–6 parts. Sufficient ammonia should be added to the bichromate solution just to start a change of colour.

The positive is placed in position on the plate in a vacuum frame and exposed to an arc lamp. It must be remembered that for an offset plate and an original reading correctly from left to right, the positive must be placed face-up on the plate: this means that there is the thickness of the paper between the drawn design and the plate surface. Consequently it is important to arrange the illumination to give parallel rays so far as possible and consistent with reasonable economy of exposure time. The actual length of exposure must be determined by trial, but it may gradually be increased during the experimental stage until a point is reached where clear development of the image becomes difficult. Standard exposure will be slightly less than this. As a rough guide the exposure with a design on good quality tracing paper and a 3000-watt arc lamp at 24 in. is approximately eight minutes.

Every precaution must be taken against over-heating, damp and light-fog. The exposed plate is placed in water for a short period and then flowed over with a 5 per cent solution of methyl violet dye. (The dye should dissolve in water but if difficulty is experienced it can be dissolved in a small quantity of methylated spirit and then water added.) A strong solution of potassium permanganate may be used in place of the above. The purpose of the dye is to enable the process of development to be observed; development should be continued with the aid of cotton-wool and a thin paste of magnesia powder and water until the coating protected from light action by the black lines of the positive is completely washed away, leaving the zinc perfectly clean. If the print is quite satisfactory a 5 per cent solution of iron perchloride and water is flowed over the surface until the clear zinc just commences to darken, but if the original is not of the best, and extreme care has to be exercised during development in order that the background is not weakened, the plate should be carefully dried after development and gently heated or allowed to stand for as long as circumstances will permit, for the coating to harden further before applying the iron perchloride.

The application of iron will remove the dye stain, but the glue stencil will remain unaffected provided due care is taken. After washing and drying, the image will be sufficiently visible to enable any necessary spotting to be carried out; this is done with gum solution coloured with any suitable medium. When this is dry, Vandyke ink (Hunter-Penrose) is rubbed over the whole surface, using a pad of soft rag. It is very important that the ink is rubbed thoroughly and firmly into the grain of the metal. A second coating of ink which has been thickened with photo-litho or transfer ink is then applied. When rubbed quite dry the plate is immersed in water, when it will be found that the ink can be rubbed away from the stencil. A short application of 1–3 per cent solution hydrochloric acid will loosen the stencil and enable it to be washed away by light rubbing with cotton-wool. After gumming and drying, wash-out solution is applied and the plate rolled up and etched in the normal way. A similar procedure to the above but using bichromated gum is briefly described on page 230.

Type matter required for a reversing process may be pulled on transparent paper and the impression dusted with bronze powder: if the impression is on ordinary paper it will be necessary to make this transluscent by applying castor oil 1 part, turpentine 10–20 parts, or similar mixture, to the back of the paper. Special papers can be obtained for this purpose, such as Kodak "Baryta" and Typon "Proving." Both of these have an excellent surface for accepting first-class impressions, and the paper is suitable for photography either by transmitted or reflected light.

A method of producing excellent type transparencies on "Cellophane" or "Glassine" has been developed with the well-known Vandercook Cylinder Proof Press.

The system consists of pulling an impression on a rubber blanket attached to the cylinder and then feeding the transparent sheet to the grippers and special roller feed attachment. Impressions can thus be obtained on both sides of the sheet, and as these are printed simultaneously coupled with the feed being of special construction, perfect register is assured.

Usually two impressions of ink are made on the offset blanket before printing.

The formes to be printed must be locked in the chase with type-high bearers around the page and the chase must be firmly locked to the bed of the press.

Impressions from half-tone blocks have also been obtained, and have been used with entire success by photo-litho departments.

Special inks are obtainable for the purpose, and can be either the quick-drying type or a more normal offset ink which requires dusting with fine bronze powder.

It is, of course, only possible to produce first-class results with suitable equipment specially adapted for the purpose.

CHAPTER XIV

INTAGLIO ETCHING OF OFFSET PLATES

MANY firms are now almost exclusively adopting a process of etching the image into the zinc plate. The term "etching" is in this case used in its true sense, that is, an actual corrosion of the metal by chemical means. The depth of the etch is scarcely measurable, particularly as it is on a grained surface, but the claims made for the several processes are certainly justified, for the method of obtaining the etched image also enables the image elements to be formed on the plate with extreme tenacity.

The intaglio effect also affords some protection to the image from the friction of the damping and inking rollers. The fine quality and depth of the printed results, and the experience of practical machine minders, indicate that a greater quantity of ink can be built up on the offset blanket without spreading the deepest shadows or affecting the delicate quality of the lightest tones.

Several processes of obtaining such plates are offered on licence, but the general procedure is as follows. A glass or film positive is made with abrupt stencil-like change from opaque to clear film, as described in the photographic section. Type matter may consist of ink impressions on some transparent material and dusted with fine bronze powder. (See page 227.) A photographic positive is generally preferred, however. The metal is coated with a light-sensitive solution and after exposure to the positive the image is developed with either water or a special developing solution according to the particular process. The result is a negative image on zinc consisting of an insoluble coating which, after suitable treatment, acts as a resist to the subsequent etching process. The actual etch is very light but must be kept under full control. A short cleaning operation is necessary and then the plate is treated with a special varnish or greasy substance which forms the basis of the lithographic image. Special ink may be applied on top of this. The acid-resisting coating is removed by chemical means or water, and finally the plate is treated with the usual litho etch and gum ready for the machine.

Many of the methods at present in use are extremely and unnecessarily elaborate, but the simpler the method and the fewer the operations, providing each is given correct and proper attention, the less likelihood there will be of failure.

In giving the following detailed instructions, it is strongly advised that the student makes repeated tests on small plates until manipulation is carried through with precision and assurance. Some of the probable and described faults may purposely be allowed to occur on some of the plates, to indicate the critical nature of this work and the futility of overlooking small departures from correct procedure.

The grain of the plate should be the same as that usually used for negative printing, i.e. 120 or slightly finer, providing the grain is sharp and close.

Moisten the zinc plate and flow over with 5 per cent glacial acetic acid solution for 15 to 20 seconds. Thoroughly wash the plate to ensure all traces of acid or deposit being removed from the hollows of the grain. A scrubbing brush should be used, followed by a large sponge.

Coat with the following solution—

Best acacia gum	.	.	.	.	5 oz	or	125 g
Ammonium bichromate, extra pure	.			1 oz			25 g
Distilled water .	.	.	.	.	32 oz		800 c.c.

The ammonium bichromate may be dissolved in some of the water separately, and sufficient ammonia added just to start a change of colour from orange to yellow. The solution must be thoroughly filtered through lightly-packed cotton-wool in the neck of a funnel, or several thicknesses of well-washed muslin. A vacuum filter, using glass wool as the filtering medium, will be found very useful. The source of power is obtained by a special form of connexion to the water supply.

The density should be measured with a Baumé hydrometer, and according to the reading first obtained, all solutions in the future should be adjusted to agree. The suggested solution is generally suitable for a whirling speed of approximately 80 r.p.m., with a 120 grain, but the present tendency is to adjust the coating solution for a whirler speed of approximately 40 increasing to 60 r.p.m. Subsequent operations will indicate the most satisfactory whirling speed, and this must be strictly adhered to in standard practice.

The plate can be coated while on a sloping board in the sink, or on the whirler while this is rotating very slowly. Precautions must be taken to avoid bubbles; an ordinary teapot will be found extremely useful for this purpose. If a glass measure is used, a piece of moistened butter muslin may be stretched over the top. If the plate is coated over the sink, a double flow is advised.

The drying of the plate must be thorough, but attempts to speed up the drying by overheating must be avoided. Should any defects occur, these may be spotted out with bichromated gum applied with a soft camel-hair brush.

It is important that the positives used should be of first-class quality, that is, the half-tone dots must be of maximum density, and as free as possible from "fringe." The solids should have a very small, absolutely clear, pinpoint dot, and the extreme high-lights consist of small dense dots. The margins of the positives should be kept as clear as possible to minimize subsequent painting out.

Exposure will depend on the type of arc lamp used, but as a rough guide, 3 to 4 minutes with a 50-ampere open type single arc lamp at 24 in. is generally satisfactory. Full exposure is preferable to under-exposure.

Upon removal of the plate from the frame, the image can clearly be seen, and the margins of the plate are painted out with a 25 per cent solution of shellac and industrial spirit to a depth of 3 or 4 inches, or as much as the image position will allow. Any unexposed or partially exposed portions of the coating, such as that below the edges of the positive, are also painted out. An electric hot air blower will be found very useful for local drying.

The image is developed with the following—

Calcium chloride, 36 to 37° Baumé	. 40 oz	or	1000 c.c.
Lactic acid	. 2 oz		50 c.c.

A small pool of this is poured on the plate, and rapidly spread over the whole area, using a plush pad. If too small a quantity is applied, there is a possibility of the solution absorbing excessive moisture from the air, with consequent softening of the exposed portions.

The developer will penetrate or dissolve the unexposed portion in from 1 to $1\frac{1}{2}$ minutes, and frothing occurs. After about 3 minutes' action, the developer is removed with a squeegee and a fresh quantity applied, which is also spread and kept moving over the plate until a total developing time of about 5 minutes has been given.

The developer is removed as completely as possible with a squeegee, followed by cotton or clean rag, and the etch applied immediately. The use of industrial spirit for removing developer is an unnecessary waste of time, and in this particular process must definitely not be included, as it would dissolve the shellac which has been used for painting out, and spread this over the image to be etched.

The etching solution is made up as follows—

Calcium chloride, 38 to 40° Baumé	. 40 oz		1000 c.c.
Iron perchloride, lump . .	. 1¼ oz	or	30 g
Chemically pure hydrochloric acid	. ¾ oz		18 c.c.

The iron perchloride may be broken into a powder to assist solution.

The etching solution is applied and spread evenly from one side of the plate to the other. It is important to see that the etch is applied evenly, and undue haste need not be attempted, provided the removal of the etch and subsequent cleaning is commenced at the same side as the first application. Any one portion of the plate will then have received exactly the same etching time as the remainder. An etching period of about 1 minute will be found satisfactory. Exceptionally deep etching is of no advantage and causes trouble in several directions, both in the preparation of the image and in eventual regraining.

If an exceptionally deep etch has been attempted, however, an oxide deposit will have formed, and this must be removed with—

Turpentine . . .	. 16 oz		400 c.c.
Alcohol (industrial spirit) .	. 16 oz	or	400 c.c.
Lactic acid	. 1 oz		25 c.c.
Acetic acid	. 2 oz		50 c.c.

This is thoroughly worked over the plate, using a plush pad specially for the purpose, and is followed by cleansing with industrial spirit as described below.

For normal procedure the foregoing paragraph can be disregarded, and after removal of the etch with a squeegee, industrial spirit is applied and rubbed over the plate with cotton-wool. (One of the cheaper brands of cotton-wool can be used for this purpose.) A second or third application of spirit is necessary to ensure the zinc being absolutely clean, and free from all traces of calcium chloride.

During this operation the stopping-out shellac will be

dissolved and spread over the image during the first application of spirit, but is practically washed away during the second application. The plate must not be allowed to dry at this stage, and after the final cleaning with spirit, a very small quantity of *fresh* pure turpentine is rubbed thoroughly over the whole surface.

If any portions not to be printed have inadvertently been etched, these may be painted out with ordinary gum solution and dried.

A small quantity of H.L. Reversing Ink or finest quality wash-out solution is spread over the surface and vigorously rubbed into the image. As thorough amalgamation of the ink with the etched metal is the most important stage of the process, a little extra time spent here will be an advantage, and it is advised that turpentine be now applied, and the design thoroughly scrubbed with a pad. Reversing ink is again applied, and rubbed well into the image, leaving as little as possible on the surface of the gum stencil. Finally, a coating of liquid photo transfer ink or photo-litho ink, reduced with turpentine, is applied in the same manner, again leaving as little as possible on the stencil surface.

After dusting with French chalk the plate is immersed in water for as long a period as convenient, and then by rubbing with a felt pad or mutton cloth the ink can be removed from the stencil. Further soaking, particularly in warm water, would loosen the stencil sufficiently for it to be removed easily, but in practice it will be found advisable to apply a 3 per cent solution of hydrochloric acid for a few seconds. This will loosen the stencil and allow it to be removed without any fear of small gum particles remaining in the hollows of the grain. A 5 per cent or 10 per cent solution of citric acid may also be used for the same purpose.

After washing and drying, the plate is treated in the usual manner with litho etch and gum.

Even if the etched portions are thoroughly clean and readily accept ink, there is always the possibility that the final acid treatment will weaken the lithographic image. Further, if only a very thin film of ink is deposited the transferrer, who frequently handles the plate for the next process, would consider it necessary to "nurse" the image. To overcome this real or apparent difficulty, it is possible to build up the finest dots and lines with a strong film of ink as follows—

The normal inking process must, as explained, be carried through to leave as little ink as possible on the gum surface. This is quickly removed with a moist pad of mutton cloth and rubbing continued with a small quantity of transfer or similar ink reduced with litho varnish, much in the same way as litho transfers are often "rubbed up." The result is a very strong and full deposit of ink on the design which thoroughly protects the basic lithographic image and permits a much stronger application of acid than would otherwise be possible.

It is advisable to make a few trials on small plates until proper manipulation is satisfactorily acquired. Under certain conditions, such as a porous coating due to poor-quality gum or traces of moisture at earlier stages, it may be difficult to free the stencil surface entirely of ink.

These conditions would prove a difficulty in any case, and by judicious use of a more liquid ink during part of the wet rubbing-in process, the image can be made to retain a good deposit with only a light broken film on the gum which is readily penetrated by side action of the acid.

General Remarks

Humidity is an important factor in the successful operation of intaglio etching, and every effort must be made to maintain this at a convenient constant; usually about 50 per cent relative humidity is satisfactory. If the plate is inadvertently overheated during drying, the gum should be washed off and the plate recoated; but if the plate is only slightly overheated, it may be allowed to stand for 10 minutes or so before commencing exposure. This precaution should be taken in all cases where several prints have to be made. Otherwise, the several exposures made on coatings of a different moisture content, and consequently of different sensitivity, will lead to apparent under- and over-exposures.

Only the highest grades of acacia gum should be used, and if powdered, this will dissolve overnight.

To determine correct exposure in the first place a test plate should be made with three or four varying exposures. If all other manipulations are carried through exactly as described, an over-exposure will show a final very sharp image, and an under-exposure will result in a soft, spongy resist, which will allow the etch to penetrate and finally result in a thickened image.

Development will be found to vary with temperature, and standard times should be tabulated for any variations experienced.

Full development after full but not over-exposure is preferable to under-exposure and under-development.

Where instructions include the use of industrial spirit, it is important that this is used, and not ordinary methylated spirit, which has far too large a water content.

Procedure after final removal of the stencil follows standard practice, i.e. the plates can either be etched, gummed and put on the machine immediately, or gummed, dried, washed out, rolled up, etc.

Faults

Acid solution penetrating the resist—Gum coating too thin. Insufficient exposure. Water in the developer or etch. Unsuitable (soft dot) positive.

Too much general contrast—Unsuitable positives. Insufficient exposure. Too vigorous an application of the pad during developing or etching. Too thick a coating. Penetration of the resist by etching solution. Insufficient cleaning after etching.

Design too strong—Under-exposure.

General appearance weak, but individual dots firm—Over-exposure.

Ink not holding and design not firm—Insufficient cleaning with oxide remover or spirit. Weak application of reversing ink. Ink reduced with oxidized or poor quality turpentine. Too long an application of acid when removing the stencil. Water in cleaning spirit.

White streaks—Small quantities of developer or other liquids being brushed across the plate from the back edges during cleaning.

Dark streaks or round marks—Etching solution allowed to remain on the plate without spreading.

Difficulty in removal of stencil—Overheating at any stage. Coating too thin.

In view of the parallel lines on which experimenters have been working, much of the foregoing will doubtless form part of processes at present being sold under licence, but it is believed that the eventual and generally adopted procedure will conform to the described operations.

Fish glue is preferred to gum by some workers, and is at present in fairly wide use, together with special proprietary varnishes. The general procedure is a combination of the processes described in this and the previous chapter.

A very interesting reversal process is associated with plates supplied by J. J. Huber. These are of thin aluminium, with a suitable grain for general work, and are sold ready coated with a light-sensitive emulsion and the particularly interesting features are that the coating is rendered soluble by the action of light, and with proper precautions it will keep in good condition for twelve months or more.

This type of emulsion enables an intaglio etched design to be obtained from a negative, and although it is, of course, advised that negatives of maximum density be used, it is possible to obtain workable results from negatives that would be considered very doubtful for the normal albumen process. The general manipulations follow standard practice regarding development, cleaning, etching, inking, etc., but special solutions are supplied and a full exposure is necessary—say twice that for an albumen print.

An uncoated plate for use with the albumen process, or for transferred designs has an anodized surface which, for all practical purposes, does not oxidize, and has the characteristic feature of retaining moisture in a similar manner to a litho stone: these are advantages which are specially valuable on the printing machine.

Providing the design has not been deep-etched, these plates can be cleaned by chemical means, and used several times, without resurfacing.

Bimetal Plates

Zinc and aluminium plates possess qualities similar to the original litho stone. The greasy image accepts a greasy ink and the water-sensitive areas of the plates repel the ink from the inking roller. The image transferred to the rubber blanket or paper surface is therefore dependent upon the variation between a wet and a greasy surface. The wet area requires continual remoistening and this factor creates control difficulties for the machine operator. Also, the greasy image can be worn away as a result of friction with the blanket or maladjustment of the water and ink supply. With this in view, attempts have been made to use bimetal or multimetal surfaces to plates whereby the properties of water- or grease-acceptance or alternatively repellence have been made use of. It can be readily seen, therefore, that if a thin image of copper is produced on the surface of a sheet of stainless (chromium) steel, then the inking roller will deposit ink on the copper fret, or image, and very little water will be needed to aid the steel in its repellent action.

Bimetal plates, based on the above general principle, have now proved to be eminently successful, giving fine definition, and the additional processing involved proves most economical when it is found that the image is practically indestructible, thereby ensuring considerably longer life on the press.

For outputs of considerable quantities the process is being adopted, and its general processing, while patented in various forms, follows basically the preparation of a "deep etch" plate.

CHAPTER XV

PROOFING

When sets of colour plates require proofing many firms prefer to do this on an offset machine or power-operated proof press such as the "Deffa," which has automatic damping and inking. This obviates the difference in results which frequently occurs between hand-proofed and machine-proofed plates; to roll up a plate by hand and obtain similar results to those obtained in a machine requires considerable skill and judgment. In fact, the skill of the proofer might even be taken too far, and following selective inking, etc., better proofs furnished of inferior plates than can subsequently be obtained on the machine.

Hand offset presses are still widely used, however, and the general arrangement comprises two bed plates, one (the plate bed) for the litho plate, and the other (the printing bed) for the paper. A metal cylinder over which a rubber blanket is stretched can be passed over the two bed plates. A gear wheel at each end of the cylinder engages with a rack, and the whole should be designed and constructed to ensure perfect register at each travel. On some machines the cylinder is raised during the return, but on the press illustrated the cylinder gearing is so arranged that disengagement takes place and the cylinder does not rotate on the return and clears the bed plates by reason of the cylinder gap being at the bottom.

Pressure in addition to the weight of the cylinder itself is regulated by both a spring on each end bearing and vertical adjustment of one or both bed plates for which hand wheels and screws are provided.

General operation is as follows. Presuming the printing bed

is a fixture, the springs controlling the pressure of the cylinder are adjusted until two strips of paper placed on the printing bed are firmly gripped. The cylinder is then brought over the plate bed and this with the plate in position is raised by the adjusting screws until a firm and equal pressure is obtained at each corner.

If the blanket is new it should first be well rubbed with finest pumice powder and water until the surface presents a smooth dull appearance. Plenty of bench room is required near the press for inking slabs and various materials used throughout.

All modern presses are fitted with grippers between which the plate can be stretched; or if a small plate is being used it may be clamped by the leading edge only. When using plates smaller than the beds, care must be taken that no sharp or buckled edges are allowed to indent the blanket. Buckles should be lightly hammered down and a file passed over all edges. If no grippers are provided on the plate bed, or, as is frequently the case, a litho stone is used for the same purpose, the plate can be firmly secured by first gumming the bed surface, laying a sheet of thin paper on this, gumming the paper and pressing the plate in position by passing the cylinder over two or three times.

Both nap and glazed rollers are used, but preference is now being given to a special type of composition roller ("Ideal" or "Mintite") which feeds the ink well and has the advantage that it can be cleaned in the minimum amount of time when changing colour. Good quality offset inks should be used, and if possible applied without reduction with mid-litho varnish or any of the mediums which are adopted so readily, and frequently to excess, by workers who have had to use inks not up to modern standards.

If the plate is not already "under wash-out" it is first washed with water, dried, thinly gummed, again dried and washed out with asphaltum solution (wash-out solution). A small quantity of water is applied with the damping sponge and spread evenly with a damping cloth (cleaned mutton cloth). The surface of

"IMPERIAL" OFFSET PROOF PRESS

the plate should only be damp; too much water will cause scumming and weakening of the ink, particularly where the edge of the roller passes over the plate. The roller, which has been charged by well rolling on the slab, is passed over the plate with a firm even pressure. The plate will probably require redamping before the image is sufficiently charged. The roller should be applied very lightly when completing the inking. The amount of rolling which can follow one damping will be determined by experience and will vary according to atmospheric conditions. Should inking inadvertently be taken too far and ink be deposited on the clear portions of the plate which have dried, the surface must be damped slightly and the roller allowed to pick up the surplus ink rather than an attempt made to rub the ink away with the damping cloth as this would probably cause spreading of the ink and uneven deposits. If this occurs an impression may be made direct to paper to remove the surplus ink, or the plate gummed, dried, and washed out with asphaltum solution, or if the image is in good condition the ink may be removed with pure turpentine and water and the inking process recommenced.

When the image is charged satisfactorily the cylinder is brought to the rear of the press and with an even steady movement passed over the plate. The ink transferred to the rubber blanket by one operation will not be sufficient for retransferring to the paper and it will be necessary to repeat the operation of damping, inking and transferring to the blanket. If there appears to be a sound impression on the blanket, a sheet of paper is positioned on the printing bed and held by the grippers; the cylinder is passed over this to the completion of its travel where with certain types of machine it is automatically raised, or the gap will be in the correct position ready for the return, during which the cylinder does not rotate. The impression on paper will probably be found to be rather weak at first, but this is better than being too heavy. In fact, the student should gradually work up to standard regarding quantity of ink on the roller and plate, and pressure on the plate and paper. If the paper impression is persistently weak at one end or corner, careful examination of the blanket impression will indicate whether the plate bed or the impression bed requires adjustment. If the blanket (assumed to be in good condition) is not receiving the ink evenly, the plate bed must be raised slightly. If on the other

THE "DEFFA" OFFSET PROOF PRESS

This machine is provided with automatic inking and damping, the inking system being operated by separate motor, to ensure full distribution. Operating speed is 200 to 300 impressions per hour, and consequently the machine can be used for short runs. The cylinder can be arranged at will to travel continuously or be interrupted at the end of each travel. Both beds are spring mounted, and have independent screw adjustments for height. This allows perfect impressions to be obtained on all types of surface and material.

hand the blanket is fully charged but not transferring evenly, then the printing bed requires adjustment or, if no adjustments are provided here, increased tension must be given to one cylinder spring. Following the latter adjustment it may be necessary to lower the corresponding end of the plate bed to avoid excessive pressure on this. Too much pressure is indicated by general spreading of the design. If spreading occurs in the lengthwise direction only, the most probable cause is a loose blanket, or a blanket of the wrong thickness. To obtain the necessary tension on the blanket considerable force has to be applied to the tensioning device incorporated. After increasing blanket tension the surface should be cleaned before recommencing work. Special blanket washes can be obtained and these should always be used in preference to solvents of doubtful nature which may seriously damage the rubber. In the absence of these, water and paraffin may be employed. Whatever is used, however, should be applied as sparingly as possible and wiped off immediately, otherwise the blanket will tend to become spongy or swollen and unsuitable for good work. After washing the blanket, pure precipitated sulphur must be dusted over the surface.

When all adjustments have been made and the blanket is both taking and retransferring the ink correctly, it should only be necessary to damp and roll up once for each impression.

The method of registering for colour work will depend to a certain extent on the type of press employed. The first colour is printed in the normal manner, but if front and side lays are provided on the printing bed the paper must be carefully registered to these. The second plate is placed as nearly as possible in the same position as the first by measurement of the register marks to fixed points on the press. The adjustable paper stops will enable the registration of the printed design to be perfected. If adjustable lays are not incorporated an impression may be made direct to the printing bed surface which has been white enamelled or to a sheet of paper which has been gummed in position. The sheets can now be registered over the impression after first punching a hole in the centre of the top and bottom register marks for sighting purposes. When the paper is laid in position in the above manner it is sometimes advisable to place another strip of thin paper over the leading edge to minimize the risk of the registered sheet being displaced as the cylinder first comes into contact with it.

When printing on thick card, metal, etc., which cannot be registered by sighting, and if adjustable lays are not provided, three small strips of slightly thinner card may be gummed to the bed—two for the leading edge and one for the side lay. These act as register stops against which the edges of the printing material can be positioned. It is often advisable, particularly when printing on metal, to provide a cut-out mask of the same material. This can act as a registering device and as a means of preventing indentation of the rubber blanket.

INDEX

A new Edition
of the greatest of all books
on photography

PHOTOGRAPHY
Theory & Practice

By L. P. CLERC, Hon.F.R.P.S.
Edited by A. KRASZNA-KRAUSZ

This masterpiece of technical translation is
certainly the most important publishing event in
the photography field for nearly twenty years.
In one superbly produced volume is detailed
yet lucid information on every aspect of
photography, on its apparatus, processes, and
many of its applications. Illustrated and fully
indexed, this encyclopaedic work should be
in the possession of all who practise or study
photography as a science and an art.

70/- net.

PITMAN
Parker Street . Kingsway . London, W.C.2

See this **WET**

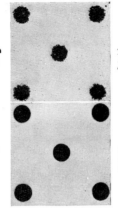

*Typical shadow dots,
150-line screen,
on wet-plate*

See this **DRY**

*Typical shadow dots
150-line screen, on
Ilford Formalith*

These two illustrations make headline news. Compare the dense, fringe-free " dry-plate " dots below with the ragged " wet-plate " dots above—here is convincing proof of an outstanding technical achievement.

THE SECRET LIES IN ILFORD FORMALITH—

A New Emulsion plus A New Developer

The name " Formalith " describes a group of Ilford products specially intended for use in photolithography and other branches of the graphic arts. The range comprises the G.71 Formalith plate, G5.71 Formalith film (on 5/1000 in. shrink-resisting base) and Formalith developer.

Ilford Formalith Emulsion. Formalith plates and films are coated with an emulsion designed to work with a special formaldehyde-hydroquinone developer. This combination of "dry-plate" emulsion and developer is capable of producing exceptionally sharp, dense dots and clean, well-defined lines without intensification or reduction. The quality of these fringeless, hard-edged images is superior to anything obtainable with the wet collodion process—and, in addition, Formalith offers all the advantages of " dry-plate " emulsions, made and coated under meticulously controlled conditions.

Ilford Formalith Developer. Specially prepared for use with Formalith plates and films, this formaldehyde-hydroquinone developer is available ready-packed in powder form. It is easy to mix and pleasant to handle.

*An informative 12-page booklet, with many striking illustrations
of what Formalith can do, will gladly be sent on request*

ILFORD FORMALITH

— in the Service of the Graphic Arts

The name FORMALITH is a registed trade mark

ILFORD LIMITED · ILFORD · ESSEX

JOHNSON

CHEMICALS FOR THE
PHOTO-LITHOGRAPHER

F OR over three-quarters of a century Johnsons
have supplied the photographic and allied indus-
tries with the chemicals required for their craft.
JOHNSON SILVER NITRATE has for many years
been accepted throughout the process trade as the
standard of purity for this important re-agent. JOHN-
SON PROCESS COLLODIONS are sent out with the
same guarantee of purity and efficiency under the
SCALES BRAND trade-mark. Johnson developers are
in use all over the world. No matter what you need
photographically, Johnsons have a chemical for it.

| SILVER | NEGATIVE | 'LINE' |
| NITRATE | COLLODION | COLLODION |

AMMON.   IRON PERCHLORIDE
BICHROMATE   (LIQUID AND SOLID)

ACID PYRO.   METOL   HYDROQUINONE

GLYCIN   AMIDOL

ETC. ETC.

JOHNSONS OF HENDON LTD.   Estab. 1743

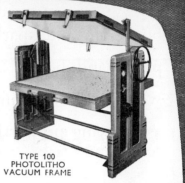

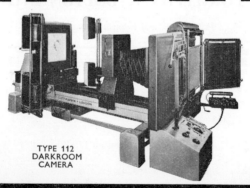